Radiant Women of Color

Radiant Women of Color

Embrace, enhance, and enjoy the beauty of your total being

by Gracie Cornish

Dr. Gracie Cornish

KOLA PUBLISHING

NEW YORK · NEW YORK

Published by:
KOLA PUBLISHING
610 FIFTH AVENUE · P.O. BOX 4739
NEW YORK, NY 10185-0040

Printed by:
NORTHEAST IMPRESSIONS
39 KULICK ROAD
FAIRFIELD, NJ   07004

Editor: Helen Bungert
Cover Layout: Liz Yasuda
Cover Illustration: Leroy Campbell
Makeup Illustrations (pgs. 46, 49): Gracie Cornish
Author's photograph: Sam Lahoz

Special thanks for permission to reprint the following:
The Right Spot original painting by **Leroy Campbell** with permission from
     THINGS GRAPHICS, Washington, D.C., page 114
Mother Earth ©1991, original painting by **Lisa Iris** with cooperation of
     SPIRIT ART, Mpls, MN, page 142
Isis ©1991, original painting by **Lisa Iris** with cooperation of SPIRIT ART,
     Mpls, MN, page 14

DEDICATION

To my daughter, Dena...and to my sisters of color who have found the unwavering love to embrace, enhance, and enjoy the beauty of their total being...and for those still searching...

ACKNOWLEDGMENTS

Warmest appreciation to the following individuals for their generous contributions, support, and interest in this project: Malcolm Whitaker, Angelena Cornish, Dureen McCalla, Helen Bungert, Heather Turnbull, Liz Yasuda, Angela Dean, Karen Wilkerson, Gabrielle Cazeau, and Audrey Edwards.

And special thanks to my daughter, Dena Danielle Cornish, for being born into my life at the same time this book was being born into the world.

FOREWORD

Beauty is not so much the graceful symmetry of physical features as it is an affirming attitude--a tireless passion and zest for life that starts within and radiates outward. How we look is typically the first reflection of how we feel, which is why such qualities as optimism, confidence and a positive sense of self contribute as much to good looks as the enhancing art of makeup.

As an editor at *Essence* magazine, the monthly service publication devoted to women of color, I know that looking good begins with loving and embracing the radiant diversity of our beauty in all its delicious hues: deep chocolate brown; smooth butterscotch; sweet peaches and cream. But loving and embracing our beauty also means caring for it. And this first means a commitment to doing those things that enhance our looks naturally--proper diet, regular exercise, adequate rest--as well as understanding the important role cosmetics and makeup play in accentuating good looks.

On the following pages, image consultant Gracie Cornish has devised a timeless, holistic beauty program for the radiant woman of color that incorporates advice on lifestyles, makeup, and clothing, and helps women to achieve their personal best in body, mind, and soul.

Here's to being all that you can be-- in all your brilliant colors of radiant beauty!

--Audrey Edwards
Editor-at-Large,
Essence Magazine

TABLE OF CONTENTS

CONTENTS

Part Two:
Embracing Your Psychological Self

Part Three:
Enjoying Your Total Being

INTRODUCTION

Dear Sister,

Black women have been shown disrespect for far too long. This disrespect comes not only from other ethnic groups, but also from our own peers. It has undermined our families, and eroded our sense of worth. *Radiant Women of Color* is designed to erase the old physical and psychological stigmas against Black women, and replace them with a new awareness of positive virtues.

This guide confronts and dispels the myths that have been long accepted as the so-called beauty standard. It explains a new approach to beauty, by guiding you to understand and appreciate the magnificence of your beautiful melanic skin. It tells you how to keep it young and healthy-looking at any age, and how to properly select and apply the right makeup and clothing suitable to your individual form.

Radiant Women of Color will help you to nurture your inner self, so you can plan your life exactly as you choose to live it. It discusses the importance of bonding with your fellow sisters and explains how you can affirm your community and family, and make America a better place for present and future generations.

It ventures deep within your very center, and teaches you how to build a compatible relationship with your mate. You will be free to express the totally beautiful being you were born to be. In short, *Radiant Women of Color* will show you how to develop timeless beauty, by creating harmony among your mind, body, and soul.

Here's to celebrating the radiance of your total being.

With love,

Gracie

1
Magnificent Melanin

I am black, and comely…because the sun
hath looked upon me…

Song of Solomon 1:5:6

1
Magnificent Melanin

As a Black woman, in America, you are faced with two major hurdles. You must first overcome the psychological beauty myth of being of African descent, and then you must meet the physical beauty standards this society expects of a woman.

Although the once enormous impact of the porcelain-skinned, blonde-haired, blue-eyed American ideal is steadily making room for other types of beauty, the strong effects of this standard, still influences the lives of many African Americans.

Many Black women have been led to believe that their features and complexions are less than ideal. This has caused confusion, pain, and sometimes even self-hatred. Women become discontented, depressed, silently wishing to look more like society's ideal.

Most African Americans, from the darkest to the lightest, are severe critics of their looks. They compare themselves to magazine pictures, television images, other women, and they inevitably fall short. They do not realize that most of these images are the result of proper makeup and lighting. By comparing themselves to these models, they are unfairly judging themselves. The pictures you see in fashion magazines are air-brushed and retouched several times.

When companies advertise the "ideal look," they are selling a product that the model is either wearing or representing. To get you to make the purchase, they have to convince you that the model represents beauty, and that you can be "beautiful" too, if only you would wear or eat what she wears or eats. It is a very effective selling gimmick. Statistics show that Black women alone, spend $600 million a year on cosmetics. This is at least three times the amount spent by any other ethnic group, yet Blacks are less than one-tenth of the entire American population.

Have you ever wondered why certain women, who are far outside this so-called "beauty ideal," are considered beautiful while others are not? However varied their appearances may be, there is something about them that is undeniably appealing. Men desire them and other women admire them. These women have discovered how to effectively enhance the features with with they have been naturally blessed. They have learned to master the secret of true beauty-- a timeless beauty which reflects the harmony between their minds and bodies. These sisters are enjoying their regal beauty as did our ancient mothers and radiant women of color-- Isis, Makeda, Nefertiti, and Cleopatra.

Melanin is the substance that gives Black humans their coloring. Four of the most legendary and beautiful women in history had richly melanic skins:

ISIS - Some historians claim she was the original mother of all civilization. All nations have sprung from her womb. She is revered as the Egyptian goddess who gave birth to astrology.

MAKEDA - ruled Ethiopia from approximately 960 B.C. to 930 B.C. The Old Testament records the story of the beautiful and rich queen who traveled from Africa to Israel to meet the very wise and rich King Solomon. In the Bible she is referred to as the Queen of Sheba. To ancient Moslems, she is Bilqis. To the Greeks, she is known as the Black Minerva. And in her homeland she was embraced as Queen Makeda, the beautiful. She gave birth to Solomon's son, Menelik. Her descendants have ruled the kingdom of Ethiopia throughout time, except for a brief period during the ninth and tenth centuries. Her beauty, her sense of adventure, and her resourcefulness have yet to be surpassed by any queen in history.

NEFERTITI – ruled Egypt along with her husband, the Pharaoh Akhenaton, from 1379 B.C. to 1362 B.C. She was a woman of great beauty, wealth, and power. There is a renowned life-size bust of her in a museum in Berlin. It is a masterpiece, reflecting her enchanting dark eyes, bronze-colored skin, and graceful neck. Queen Nefertiti will always be remembered for her beauty, as well as for her power.

CLEOPATRA – One of the most controversial and seductive women known to history, she was born in 69 B.C. and became queen of Egypt at the age of 18. Historically known for her political and sexual relations, she used her beauty, wit, and knowledge to keep the Roman Empire from destroying her beloved Egypt. Although she has been dead for over two thousand years, her legend lives on through many mediums including, 14 Cleopatra plays, 3 Cleopatra films, and over 1060 Cleopatra poems.

Although sprinkled throughout different times in history, these legendary women all had one thing in common-- their beautiful melanic skins.

Melanin is the dark pigment in the outer layer of the skin in Black humans. Each person's skin color is determined by three pigments: melanin, carotene, and hemoglobin. Melanin gives a brown coloring. Carotene contributes a yellowish hue. And hemoglobin lends a reddish tone to the skin. The more melanin one has, the deeper the skin complexion.

The range of natural coloring for each ethnic group depends on the varying amounts of each of the three pigments. Black women have mostly brown pigment in their skin. Caucasian women have some red and yellow. Hispanic and Indian women tend to have more red and brown. And Asian women have an abundance of yellow and a touch of brown.

Many Blacks have negative feelings about their melanic skins because of the problems, discomforts, and false standards they have experienced in Western society. Their color has been the cause of much suffering, oppression, and even bloodshed. But the truth is, melanin is a magnificent chemical that lends a lovely brown tint to the skin. If this coloring is so negative, why do so many people of other ethnic groups lie hours upon hours in the sun or in tanning salons, in hopes of obtaining a rich melanic glow? Many even run the risk of contacting skin cancer by overexposure to damaging ultraviolet rays.

Melanic skin ranges from golden-bronze to bluish-black. The properties of melanin are increased by light energy, either from the sun or from artificial light like an ultraviolet

(UV) or infrared light bulb (similar to the ones used in tanning salons). People with higher degrees of melanin are less susceptible to skin cancer, premature aging, and sagging skin. Their skins retains a youthful glow over a longer period of time.

One of the biggest myths, however, is that Black skin is made for the sun, and, therefore, the sun cannot damage it. This is not true. Although Black skin can tolerate greater degrees of exposure to U.V. rays than can lighter, it still needs to be protected-- either by applying a mositurizing lotion or by wearing proper clothing.

THE PROPER CARE OF YOUR SKIN

If we were asked to state our body's important organs, we would most likely list the heart, kidneys, lungs, liver, etc., and would probably not mention the skin. But the fact is the skin is very vital. It is the body's largest organ. It protects our internal organs, assists in eliminating poisons, and regulates our body temperature. It also shows our beauty.

The skin has millions of pores through which toxins from decomposed body cells are released. Just below the skin's surface are millions of sweat glands, constantly work-ing to filter the impurities and poisons from our blood-stream. When we perspire, some of these toxins, or dead cells, are released from our body through our pores. If the

20

skin is not properly cleansed, the dead cells will accumulate and continue to build up on the skin's surface, leaving an ashy film. This may eventually clog the pores, or the poisons may be reabsorbed into the blood, contaminating the body system.

Unclean skin is very dangerous to our well-being. One should not depend on cosmetics to clean or purify the skin. Cosmetics can only enhance clean, healthy skin. Proper skin care begins on the inside-- keeping our systems clean and healthy with the aid of nature's basic remedies of herbs, proper vitamins, minerals, pure water, fresh air, and sleep.

There is a very old and wise saying, "What's in the blood, must come out in the skin." One has to bloom from the inside out, not from the outside in.

One of the chief ways of achieving healthy skin is to properly cleanse our systems. Plums, raisins, avocados, and dry-roasted unsalted peanuts are among the best of nature's remedies. Not only do they clear the body system, but they also help to build it. Raisins are a good source of vitamin C, and peanuts are rich with protein. The ashy, or flaky, skin that many African Americans suffer from, is due to the large content of fried and greasy foods in their diets. The fat residue from these types of foods are poisonous to the body's system, and result in poor digestion and improper elimination; leaving a grayish film on the skin's surface. Any type of green leafy vegetables (especially spinach), will help to prevent this formation on the skin and give it a soft texture by breaking down the fatty substances. Vegetables also furnish the body with many vital nutrients.

Although there are many wonderful skin-care products on the market today, unfortunately most are not prepared with the consumer's well-being in mind. The company's profit is the major consideration. Many cosmetics companies seem to be involved in a money-making marathon, competing to see which can out-do the others with the most captivating product packaging. The actual effect of the product on people's skins is not the main focus. Each season you can look forward to a supposedly "new and scientifically-improved breakthrough." The representatives who create the names of some of these products show remarkable ingenuity. But, some are downright laughable. However, what should not be applauded is the fact that women spend unnecessary amounts of money on these products. And it is no laughing matter that these women expect to discover beauty in these skin-care jars, only to find out that these products can not live up to their claims.

We have been offered *skin-renewing, skin-correcting,* and *skin-balancing* creams-- *anti-aging, youth-retaining, instant-acting* and *lasting-action* skin gels. There are the bizarre sounding ones, such as *micro-refining, macro-defining, past-correcting* and *future-adjusting.* Then there are some with such complicated compositions that the consumer would need a medical dictionary to properly decipher the intricate ingredients.

And if that weren't enough, there are creams also being marketed for individual body parts: *face cream, eye cream, body cream, hand cream, nail cream, foot cream, cuticle cream, throat cream, chest cream, cellulite cream,* and, of course, the ever popular *complexion-bleaching cream.* Many of these claim to be approved by "prominent lab specialists." That's fine, but none of them work any better than the basic skin-care products available in the drug or health-food stores. It is all clever packaging and marketing, to entice you into buying.

You must read labels before buying any product. If you don't understand the purpose or the benefit of each ingredient, don't put it on your skin. Your skin is too important not to be properly cared for. Start caring for it today, that your skin may remain deliciously pleasing tomorrow.

THE SECRET TO CLEAN, YOUTHFUL, AND
HEALTHY-LOOKING SKIN AT ANY AGE

Our bodies are the temples of our minds and spirits. These houses should be kept clean, attractive, beautiful and healthy-looking. Here are two simple, straightforward, no-nonsense approaches to good skin care-- one is for the body, the other for the face. I will not give you any drawn-out or overstated routines as most beauty books or cosmetics counter representatives do. If you have severely sensitive skin, or a skin ailment of any kind, see a dermatologist or homeopathic doctor before using this or any other skin-care method. This is a basic routine to keep your skin clean, fresh, and young-looking.

You don't have to spend a fortune to look good. The steps I'm giving you here, have been proven to work wonders. They will make your skin reflect radiant beauty. They will save you time and money.

FOR THE BODY:
1. Shower daily with fresh water and pure Castile soap (available in most health food stores).
2. Once a week, gently massage your entire body with a natural loofa bath sponge (available in most drug or health food stores). Do not use nylon or synthetic bristle brushes, because the fibers are very abrasive and may irritate the skin. The loofa is a vegetable gourd, dried and processed into an all-natural massager and exfoliator. It becomes a soft sponge when wet. It stimulates healthy circulation at the skin's surface. It cleanses away dirt and dead skin cells with tiny fibers, and it helps to prevent clogged pores as it smoothes and softens the skin. It also works very well on rough areas such as elbows and knees. After your loofa massage, take a relaxing bath in pure Castile liquid soap and a few drops of virgin olive oil for about 30 minutes.
3. Two or three times weekly, indulge in a pleasantly

scented bath of essential oils extracted from various flowers, plants, leaves, or roots. These natural aromatic fragrances added to your bath water will relax and refresh your senses, and enliven your skin's glow.

4. Three or four times weekly, lotion your entire body with a combination of pure peanut oil and rose water. The peanut oil will give your skin a soft, wholesome glow, and the rose water will give it a nice pleasant smell. *Note:* For dry, itchy skin, increase the amount of peanut oil. On the remaining days, lotion yourself with a fragrance-free moisturizer.

5. Once monthly, take an Epsom Salt deep-cleansing bath, in very warm water. Soak for about 30 minutes. The salts will help to pull out the toxins from under the skin's surface. Or, once a week, shower in pure Castile soap, dry yourself, then dip your wash cloth in a solution of Epsom Salt and water and wipe down your entire body. In both cases, rinse off the residue from the salts before moisturizing the body with pure peanut oil.

6. Daily, drink two glasses of pure pineapple juice or two cups of Rose Hips tea. These are very rich sources of vitamin C. Vitamin C helps to keep collagen strong in the body. Collagen is the substance responsible for our skin's elasticity, tightness, and youthful look.

7. Daily, drink at least six glasses of pure, unpolluted, spring water to help keep your kidneys, lungs, colon, liver, and skin clean and properly functioning. Set time aside to enjoy fresh air, exercise, and relaxation.

FOR THE FACE:

1. Enjoy looking at yourself in the mirror.
2. Daily, cleanse your face with clean water and pure Castile soap.
3. Make a paste of baking soda and water to exfoliate dead skin cells (once a week for dry skin, twice weekly for oily skin).
4. Deep-clean your pores with a facial mud mask, preferably with French Green clay as a primary ingredient (once monthly for dry skin, twice monthly for oily skin).
5. Moisturize daily with pure peanut oil or a natural fragrance-free cream (for dry skin), or an oil-free, fragrance-free lotion (for oily skin).
6. Get proper rest, moderate exercise, and smile often.

You now have the key to vibrant-looking skin. Whether you choose to adopt these two simple, natural, and effective methods, or to select some other form of basic skin-care routine, the important thing to remember is not to let package promises or advertising claims influence your choice of skin-care products. Many of these products can clog your pores, irritate your skin, or cause premature aging. Most do absolutely nothing.

A WORD ABOUT VITILIGO

Before closing this chapter, I must take time to inform you of a very damaging disease that affects people of color. It can cause serious emotional, social, and aesthetic problems.

One percent of the world, and two percent of the United States population, suffers from it.

Vitiligo, or leukoderma, is a progressive loss of skin pigmentation. It is characterized by the appearance of whitish spots on the skin. These patches occur when melanin is no longer produced. Melanin is created in the cytoplasm of melanocytes, which are special cells located in the base layer of the epidermis (the skin's surface), where it joins the dermis (an inner layer of the skin). If melanocytes can no longer form the black substance melanin, skin color will become lighter or completely white.

In vitiligo, depigmented skin areas are located mainly in the face, joints, genital regions, and hands. It may remain stationary for years, but it tends to advance slowly, spreading throughout the body. Skin affected by vitiligo is hypersensitive to ultraviolet radiation, and it can easily be burned when exposed to sunlight. People with vitiligo should protect themselves from excessive exposure to the sun with a sunscreen lotion or cream containing an SPF (Sun Protecting Formula) of 15 or higher.

The exact cause of vitiligo is not known. Many people claim to have pigment loss shortly after experiencing an emotional trauma, associated with death in the family, or a frightening accident. Some are said to experience it after a severe sunburn. Severe stress or illness can result in greater pigment loss.

To this date, there is no known cure or prevention for vitiligo. However, there are two methods that can help to restore normal color to the skin.

METHOD I: (practiced in the United States)
Patients are given a psoralen drug and then exposed to an ultraviolet light (UV-A). This is said to help stimulate repigmentation by increasing the availability of color-producing cells at the skin's surface. The psoralen drugs are *trimethyl-psoralen* and *8-methyoxypsoralen*. The patient takes a prescribed dosage, by mouth, two hours before lying in the sun or under an artificial UV-A light. About 75% of the patients who undergo psoralen and UV-A light therapy respond to some extent, but complete repigmentation rarely occurs.

If the patient has vitilligo over more than half of her body, de-pigmentation of the entire body may be suggested by some doctors. The drug used for this is *mono-benzylether*.

METHOD 2: (practiced in the Caribbean)
The treatment used to repigment affected areas is called *Melagenina.* Its composition is purified human placental biostimulins and alcohol. It is said to have a powerful repigmentation effect, capable of producing an 80% remission in severe cases of vitiligo. It can be used on children, adults, and pregnant women with no side effects.

Melegenina is in lotion form, and is applied topically over the depigmented skin areas. The affected areas are then exposed to natural sunlight or an infrared light, (250w – 120v red light- bulbs are used), for 15 minutes during each treatment. It is alleged that cutaneous repigmentation achieved in vitiligo cases is irreversible.

Further research is presently being conducted to find an alternative therapy for vitiligo, one which will help promote natural healing of the melanin-producing cells. The emphasis is on assisting the proper assimilation, circulation, and elimination processes in the body through the aid of proper nutrition and natural herbal products.

For further information on vitiligo and its treatment, send a self-addressed stamped envelope (SASE) to:

CIEE GLOBAL COMMUNICATIONS GROUP
610 Fifth Avenue
P.O. Box 4729
New York, NY   10185-0040

2
Magical Makeup

2
Magical Makeup

Looking good is important. A good makeover can open many doors for you. A properly made-up woman carries an air of prosperity. She is sought after, both personally and professionally.

Ancient Egyptian women discovered and perfected "the art of looking good." They invented cosmetics made of natural substances to increase their appeal. They applied deep green and black powders to darken their lashes and eyebrows, and to outline their eyes. They used henna to color their nails and hair; they highlighted their cheeks and dyed their lips with reddish clay-like substances. In short, they were artists who contoured their features into lovely works of art that have been revered throughout history.

There is no basic flaw that cosmetics cannot contour. Your makeup should be carefully selected to enhance your individual features, complexion, and skin texture. It should not be worn as a mask to hide behind. It should be properly applied to accentuate and bring out your natural beauty. No matter what your profession, whether artist or executive, your makeup should always look natural. It should never look distastefully blatant. If people admire your makeup, then you've not applied it properly. If they admire your beauty, then you've blended it successfully.

Try many different cosmetics lines before selecting one as your own. Go to cosmetics salons, department stores, or drugstores to try the various samples of the many exciting brands available on the market today. Many large department stores offer complimentary makeovers. Any good makeup artist should be able to guide you into selecting and applying the ones suitable for you. But make sure you ask for a trained makeup artist to work with you. All cosmetics-counter attendants should be experienced in this area, but this is not always the case. Some are only cosmetics salespersons, not cosmetics specialists.

You may wish to take a friend with you to provide a second opinion. Many women go to cosmetics outlets and are convinced by the attendants to purchase products that are supposedly right for them. Many salespeople will convince women to buy an absurd amount of unnecessary products in order to increase their own commissions. But, once home, the look seems different. Women may try the products for a few days, thinking they need time to get used to it. They may get negative reactions from their friends and families. They then realize these products are not suitable for them. The items end up being thrown away or stored in the medicine cabinet, never to be used again. These women may blame their own looks for this failure. They have wasted valuable time, energy, and money. They have lost faith in the cosmetics company and in themselves. The cosmetics company has lost a potential customer-- all because of limited cosmetics knowledge on the part of the salesperson.

The simple truth is, the majority of cosmetics salespersons are trained to talk you into buying as many products as they can. They'll tell you that you need a ridiculous and unnecessary amount of products in order to be beautifully made-up. They'll share that a certain product won't work without another, and so on. Or they'll manipulate you into buying by rattling off fabulous claims. A lot of the information is actually untrue. But don't blame the salespersons. They are trained to "build multiple sales," and are just trying to make a living.

The following is a basic overview on how to select and apply makeup that's best for you. It is important not to be misled by the packaging and promotion of the products, or by their cost. Many people mistakenly believe that if a product is more expensive, then it must be better for them. The reality is, although there are many wonderful makeup lines in department stores, many moderately-priced drugstore brands work just as well. Another important thing to keep in mind is that many of the products you may purchase from various cosmetics lines are made by the same manufacturer. The only difference is the name brand, price, and marketing of the lines.

HOW TO CHOOSE AND USE
THE RIGHT FOUNDATION FOR YOU

Although Black women are generally categorized as having either dark, medium, or light-toned skin, the Black race actually contains a color spectrum of thirty-six different shades, ranging from plum blue to creamy beige.

The purpose of foundation (base color) is to even out the skin tone and cover discolorations. African American women are generally satisfied with their choices of lipsticks and blushes, but are frequently displeased when trying to find a foundation suitable to their specific complexions.

It has become common practice for cosmetics companies to classify skin complexions by the four seasons of the year. The makeup colors are arranged and categorized in palette groupings: Spring – bright-toned colors; Summer – pastel-toned colors; Autumn – earth-toned colors; and Winter – deep-toned colors. The popular belief that the majority of Black women fall in the Winter category of the cool, deep-toned palette is not true. Some do indeed have cool undertones and are best suited with fuchsia, navy, magenta, plum, and burgundy; but many others look better in the warm, earth toned Autumn palette of bronze, copper, rust, olive, coral, warm red, and golden brown. Still others look even better in the neutral, pastel-toned Summer palette, or in the dramatic, bright-toned Spring palette. Black women shouldn't get trapped by color seasons as promoted by color analysts. Instead, they should select a foundation that complements the natural colors of their skin, hair, and eyes. Then choose colors that either blend or contrast nicely with the selected foundation.

Makeup is designed to complement both the skin tone and undertone. While the surface tone depends on how much melanin (brown hue) you possess, your undertone depends on the amount of carotene (yellow hue), and hemoglobin (red hue), pigment in your skin. Don't get distracted by the various degrees of color tones and undertones. Choose your ideal foundation by matching it against your jawline, cheeks, and the center of your forehead. Do not purchase anything until you have tested several shades in your complexion range. Select various shades that look like a good match, then place them in a row of stripes on your jawline. The one that blends exactly with your complexion, is the best choice. Next, apply it to your entire face, then check it outside in daylight or against a white background. You must check the look in natural light, because the fluorescent lighting in department stores takes a lot of red tones away and magnifies yellow tones. You will not be able to see a true picture in these artificial lights.

If your face is much lighter or darker than your neck, then the above method of choosing foundation doesn't apply to you. Many women make the mistake of applying foundation to their necks in hopes of creating a balance. Foundation should never be applied to the neck. It will look artificial, and will also soil your clothing. If your face is lighter than your neck, you should choose a slightly darker foundation to blend with the neck color. If your face is darker than your neck, you should select a lighter-toned foundation which complements the neck shade. It's always best to blend closer to the neck color, otherwise you'll look like you're wearing a mask. If the shade range between face and neck is very wide, you should choose a foundation in between both colors. Then select a finishing powder closest to the neck shade and apply it over the foundation, to create an even look.

FOUNDATION TYPES

Now that you have chosen the best foundation color for your complexion, it is time to decide which foundation formula is best for your skin type (normal, oily, or dry). There are four basic kinds of foundations available on the market today: water-based, powder-based, oil-based, and oil-free. They come in three different forms: liquid, cream, and compact.

Water-based foundation contains some oils, but its main ingredient is water. It is a slightly thick liquid, and is best suited for those with normal or slightly dry skin. It blends wonderfully, and lends a nice sheen to the face. But on oily skin, it may appear a bit too shiny.

Powder-based ideal for women with normal or oily skin. It has a nice silky texture that feels creamy, but it blends like powder on the face. It goes on quickly and easily; it blends evenly and smoothly. It stays on all day and feels natural on the skin, but it is not recommended for women with dry skin.

Oil-based foundation contains some water, but oil is the primary ingredient. It is thick, oily, and greasy. It should only be used by women with extremely dry or flaky skins. But, even for these women, it has a tendency to clog the pores, change color, and run throughout the day. It should definitely not be used by women with oily skins at any time. It tends to look unnatural and heavy on all skin types.

Oil-free foundation contains no oil at all. It gives a matte finish and is best for women with very oily skins. There are two variations of this formula on the market-- one with an alcohol base, and the other with a glycerin base. The one with the alcohol base is very fast drying, and may leave streak marks as it is applied. The glycerin-based formula provides better coverage, but also tends to blend unevenly. Both types of this oil-free foundation should be avoided if possible, because they give the face a somewhat dried-out and ashy look.

Liquid foundation gives a soft look to the face. It goes on as a very sheer and thin layer. It is best suited for those who desire minimal coverage. It is wonderful for women with no blemishes or discolorations, and for those with normal to oily skins.

Cream foundation, sometimes referred to as soufflé, is less transparent than the liquid. It can be used to cover up blemishes, and gives the skin a nice even look, when applied lightly. However, if applied too heavily, it can emphasize wrinkles and folds. It provides good coverage for all skin types.

Compact foundation can be used by women with severe facial spots or discoloration. It gives the most opaque coverage, and is the least transparent foundation. However, if it is not properly blended, it gives a mask-like appearance. Because of its heavy consistency, it should be avoided by women with oily skins, but can be used by those with normal to dry skins.

MASTERING THE ART OF BLENDING YOUR MAKEUP

Makeup is only beautiful if it is properly blended. Otherwise, it just sits on the face and looks unnatural. If there are any demarcation lines at the hairline or jawline, then you've defeated your purpose, which is to look natural.

Many women mistakenly believe that the more makeup they put on, the better the coverage. But this is not so. Makeup should be applied and shaded as lightly as possible. This is where the rule of "less is always best" holds true. Subtle is the enchantment of a beautifully madeup face. It is neither overdone nor tacky. You can master the technique of tastefully blending your makeup very easily. The trick is to use a 5-dot technique and to work quickly. Whether you are using a liquid or a cream, the procedure is the same. However, when applying cream, it's best to use a triangular-shaped makeup sponge (wedge), and when applying liquid, it is best to start with the fingers, then smooth over with a sponge.

Your sponge shouldn't be made of foam rubber, or have any holes in it. With your sponge, place one dot in the center of your forehead, one on your nose, one on each cheek, and one on your chin; start to blend immediately before the foundation starts to dry in the open air. Using light even strokes, begin from the forehead in an outward motion toward, but not into, the hairline; then move downward traveling over the folds of the eyes, to the nose,

41

outward to the cheeks, over the upper lip area, around to the chin area and finish at the jawline. Do not blend the foundation past the chin or jawline; it shouldn't be placed on the throat or neck at all. Don't rub, wipe, or pull, but instead use gentle pats, presses, and quick strokes to shade in with your natural skin tone. There should be no noticeable difference in the shading between your face, jawline, and neck. Slightly tilt your head backwards, and examine it from side to side; make sure there isn't a two-tone look between your face and neck. If you've missed any spots, or applied too much, or if you just need to blend more evenly, slightly dampen your sponge with a little water, and smooth over the entire face. When properly done, you'll have a lovely, smooth, and natural look.

15 MINUTES TO A STRIKINGLY BEAUTIFUL FACE

A strikingly beautiful face doesn't have to look bold and dramatic or mysterious and exotic. It can simply look pleasant and romantic. This technique is for a natural-looking, charming face. Natural doesn't mean naked; it means whatever products you apply must harmoniously synchronize to give a soft, lovely appearance. Once you have practiced this simple routine, you can set time aside to experiment with a wider variety of looks. You should have fun with your face. You can create and play with many different colors of eyeshadows, lipsticks, and blushes, to see their varying effects. You can tone them down, or jazz them up, and once you get the hang of it, you'll be able to perform an entire facial makeover in about fifteen minutes.

Let's start with the basic tools you'll need:
1. A clean face – makeup won't look good or stay on skin that is not properly cleansed.
2. A mirror and proper lighting.
3. A wedge sponge, Q-tip, powder brush, eyebrow brush, and facial tissues.
4. The cosmetics products you'll need are: concealer (or cover stick), foundation (base), loose powder, eyeliner, eyeshadow, mascara, eyebrow pencil, blush (rouge), lip pencil, lipstick, and pressed finishing powder.

APPLICATION IN 10 EASY STEPS

1. **Concealer** is used to camouflage any discolorations, blemishes, or dark circles under the eye area or on the eyelid. It should be blended with the fingertip, moving from the outer corner inward. It can also be used to make a wide nose appear thinner. A light shade of concealer should be applied down the center of the nose, and a dark shade should be applied on each side of the nose, and gently blended with the fingertip.

2. **Foundation** (use the method previously described).

3. **Powder** – This is to keep your makeup in place. It can also be used to give a nice matte finish. Many people believe that powder shows up wrinkles, but this is a myth. It is best

to use a loose at this stage, and a compact one for retouching when needed. You must properly blend your powder into your foundation to create a natural, uniform look. Dip your powder brush into the powder, shake off the excess, and apply to your entire face with light strokes. Make sure it's evenly spread. Next, slightly dampen a facial tissue, then pat the semi-dry tissue all over your face, including your eyelids. This will "set" the makeup, and give a more attractive look.

4. **Eyeliner** - This is used to shape, emphasize, and frame the eyes. You can choose between liquid or pencil eyeliner. The liquid is longer-lasting, but you must use a steady hand, because it is harder to apply. The pencil gives a softer, more natural look if it's blended properly. If not, it tends to smudge easily. Start from the inside corner of either eyelid, and stroke outward, just beyond the end of the eyelid. To make small eyes appear larger, do not line the bottom lid. If the area beneath your eyes is puffy or wrinkled, do not line the bottom lid either, because it will draw too much attention to the area.

5. **Eyeshadow** - Three well-blended colors will give your eyes a very appealing look. The easiest way to apply is to slightly tilt your chin toward the mirror, tilting your forehead backward. You will be able to see your entire eyelid without having to pull or wrinkle it. In this position, you can properly apply shadows with a downward glance. This will save you the mishap of applying colors only to the limited areas you are able to see when your eyes are fully opened.

Select three colors which complement each other nicely. There should be a light, a medium, and a deep-toned color. Start with the lightest shade and blend it over the entire lid, up to the brow arch. This will highlight the eye. Next, use the medium-toned color. Blend it into the crease line, and below the entire eyelid. This will accentuate the eyes. Use the darkest-toned about one-third in from the outside corner of the eyelid. Extend it slightly outward and upward. Properly blend to create a smoky effect. This will define the eyes. All three colors should flow nicely into each other; overlap the edges and smudge the edges of each color-line into the others to create a professional effect.

6. **Mascara** is used to promote longer and thicker-looking lashes. Apply by stroking up and out of outer-lash surface. Put on about three to five thin layers, but work quickly to prevent a clumpy or messy look. If any smudges onto your eyelids, or eye corners, use a Q-tip to dab away excess.

7. **Eyebrow pencil** is used to define the eyebrows, and to fill in sparse eyebrows. One of the most unattractive makeup habits that many Black women practice is to shave off their natural eyebrows and then draw an unnatural line from one end of the brow line to the other. This gives a very harsh and fake appearance. The proper use of the eyebrow pencil is to shape and fill in spaces in between natural brow hairs. If the brows are too bushy and unruly, some of the excess hair should be tweezed, plucked, or waxed. One should pluck only a minimal amount of hair. The hair should be tweezed

from under the outer edge of the brow, starting about one-third from the outer edge and plucking outward in the direction of the hair growth to create a slight arch. An eyebrow brush should be used to groom the brows. One should brush up and outward. Eyebrow pencils should be as close to the natural hair color as possible. Black eyebrow pencils should be avoided. For people with blue-black colored hair, an off-black or deep, dark-brown pencil should be used. When properly defined, the eyebrows frame the eyes nicely, and give the face a stunning look.

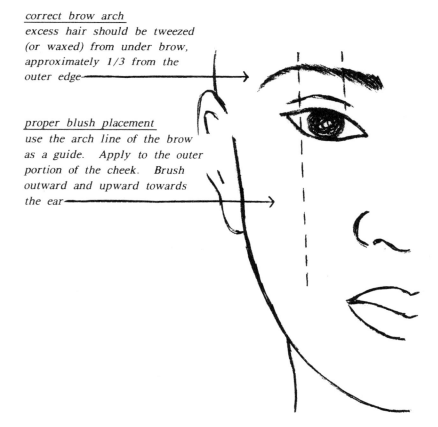

correct brow arch
excess hair should be tweezed
(or waxed) from under brow,
approximately 1/3 from the
outer edge

proper blush placement
use the arch line of the brow
as a guide. Apply to the outer
portion of the cheek. Brush
outward and upward towards
the ear

8. **Blush** is used to enhance and define cheeks. There is a choice between cream rouge and powder blusher. The cream rouge tends to go on oily, while the powdered blush gives a soft, matted look. Most women apply too much blush, which stands out blatantly, looking like clown makeup. The blush should be blended into the foundation, to add just a hint of color. It should not be applied on the front of the cheeks, but from the outer sides of the cheeks, and then stroked upward. If too much blush is applied by mistake, you can use your face powder to tone it down.

9. **Lip liner** is used to outline and define lips. It will prevent lipstick from smudging or "bleeding." It may also be used as a lipstick, to give a soft, romantic, matte look. If used without a lubricant, however, it tends to dry out the natural moisture from lips. Before applying your lipstick, cover your lips with foundation, and draw your preferred lip shape with the liner. To make lips appear smaller, draw your desired shape just *inside* the natural lip line; to make them appear larger, draw the shape just *outside* the natural lip line.

10. **Lipstick** – Along with nail polish, this is the makeup product most widely used by African American women. It is available in creme, matte, or frosted formulas. Black lips look nice with many dramatic bright shades, and with deep reds, but even better with the many natural looking earth-toned shades. Lipsticks can be applied directly form the tube onto the lips, or with a lip brush, which gives the lips a more

even look. Many Blacks have unevenly colored lips. To camouflage this, simply cover the entire lip with your foundation, then cover with your lipstick. To keep color on longer, the trick is to apply two layers. Pat the first one with a tissue, then add the second. The lips, along with the eyes, are two of the most attractive features of a woman's face.

At this point, you have the necessary know-how to create a fine work of art. You may or may not choose to apply a finishing powder as a final touch. Think of your face as your canvas, and your makeup products as the tools needed to paint a stunning masterpiece, as long ago perfected by our ancient Egyptian mothers.

THE 3-MINUTE QUICK FIX

Makeup doesn't have to take longer than three minutes to apply in order to look good. The following is my personal favorite which can be applied easily. It can be used everyday, and can be cleansed off quickly at the end of the day.

1. Clean and moisturize the face.
2. Use a compact finishing powder (one that adds color, not the translucent type), to dust entire face.
3. Brush and fill in eyebrows.
4. Apply mascara (optional).
5. Outline lips with an earth-toned color lip pencil.
6. Apply an earth-toned matte lipstick; or use a cream one and blot with a tissue to create a naked, natural look.

Brush and pencil in brow

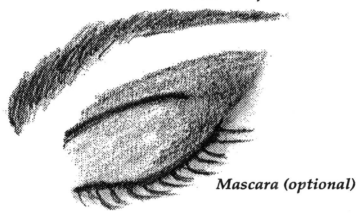

Mascara (optional)

Powder

Moisturize

Apply lipliner

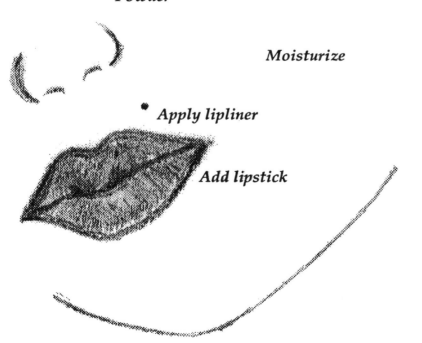

Add lipstick

To properly remove any makeup, use a gentle water-soluble cleanser blended with a touch of peanut oil; then follow the skin care steps as outlined in chapter one.

Remember, it is your birthright to be beautiful, to display a warm and radiant glow. Beauty should not cross the boundaries to self-conceit, but should venture to the point of self-confidence. As the beloved and renowned mystic, Edgar Cayce, expressed so beautifully, *"In care of self, selflessness is great. But be more mindful of the little niceties about self and you will find a pride in self - not a false pride. But as nature manifested in its Maker, it does the best it can with what it has and looks the most beautiful with what it has to do with. Thy body, too, is indeed the temple of the living God. Keep it beautiful. Be mindful of the care of same, and you - too - will think more of it.*

3
Dressing Essentials

3
Dressing Essentials

It is said you can't judge a book by its cover, but that's exactly what many of us do. There is another saying, "You may not be able to tell, but you can *sell,* a book by its cover."

Something may look valuable on the outside, but be of little worth on the inside. Or something may look unimportant on the outside, but is priceless on the inside. In ideal situations, people take the time to evaluate the content of a person's character before passing judgment, but how many idealists have you ever encountered?

Every human being, consciously or subconsciously, passes judgment on every other based, on outward appearance. Within the first few minutes of meeting, we quickly scan and evaluate another, before the person has a chance to even say a word.

We sum people up at initial contact. Each time we attend a job interview, a meeting, a date, or any social setting, we are being evaluated, just as we are evaluating others. It is natural for people to assess us by our appearances, because it reflects how we feel about ourselves.

Our appearances influence our lifestyles, our friendships, our relationships, and even our careers. The expectation to look good, whether openly stated or silently implied, is very real. Human beings are judgmental creatures. It is our nature to evaluate and conclude. We will be judged, fairly or unfairly, by our appearances. Most people live by, "the first impression is a lasting one." It may not be fair, but it is done.

Have you ever seen a man eagerly open a door for one woman, but ignore another? Or a salesperson gladly acknowledge one customer with a vibrant, "Hello ma'am, how can I help you?", but virtually disregard another? Or a supervisor may have her instructions harmoniously carried out by an employee, while another's is only grudgingly obliged?

The degree of respect you receive depends on how well you carry yourself. Take a look around you. Observe the woman who is shown the most courtesy and respect in stores, at work, or in restaurants. Her appearance tells people, "This woman is important. She is prosperous, confident, and intelligent. She respects herself; therefore I respect her."

The poorly-packaged female's appearance says, "Here is a woman who doesn't think much of herself. She is unimportant, careless, and not doing well. She is used to being overlooked, and doesn't deserve special treatment."

Your appearance tells people about you. Make sure it makes positive statements. This holds true for everything in life. Anything that looks better-packaged is assumed to be more valuable; therefore, it is given more care and respect. The next time you are in a supermarket, for example, examine the price of the fruits or vegetables nicely wrapped in polyurethane vs. the ones unwrapped. Although they are the exact same produce, I'll guarantee that the ones with the plastic coverings cost about twice as much as the unwrapped. The simple fact is the quantity of public acceptance you receive, is based on the quality of your wrapping. So make sure you are properly "wrapped" when trying to effectively market yourself.

If you want to be prosperous, start dressing pro-sperously now. Don't make the mistake of waiting to dress successfully, only after you become successful. Your goal should be to stand out from the crowd now. Be distinctive in your dressing. Good apparel gives the impression that you are a winner. You will project leadership in a silent, dignified, and unmistakable manner.

The importance of proper packaging is even emphasized in the Bible. Moses, when he was living as a prince in Pharoah's household, wore fine garments. When he became the emancipator of his people, God gave him specific details pertaining to the rich apparel that should be worn by his brother Aaron. The clothing was to be made of brilliantly colored linen with gold trimmings, worn with diamonds, emeralds, and many other precious gems.

Ancient Egyptian women were always gloriously arrayed in the finest silks, linens, and elaborate jewelry. It is actually a sin for us to dress shabbily or poorly. It cost so little to be clean and neat. We can't afford not to be. It always pays to dress prosperously. When we look good on the outside, we always feel better on the inside. We can use fine garments as an aid to boost our confidence and elevate our spirits. The effect our appearances has on our thinking is significant. For instance, a woman feels more like an executive when she is dressed like one; she feel sexier when she is dressed sensuously.

Many women mistakenly believe that they cannot look prosperous unless they can afford to wear designer clothing.

But this is not true. Let me explain a few facts about designer clothing. Each season, many new fashion trends are introduced to the market. A small circle of top designers decides which colors, styles, and fabrics will be the season's theme. The selected styles are then shown to clothing buyers and fashion reporters. They are then placed in fashion publications for consumers to absorb, and thereafter made available to the general public through clothing stores.

Although many designers make some fabulous garments, don't get hypnotized by the brand-name phenomena. As we have already seen with cosmetics, much designer clothing is made by the same factories. The only difference is the labels and price tags that are affixed to the various clothing lines. Many times we pay the high price for the exclusiveness of wearing the designer's name, instead of paying for the uniqueness of the garment itself.

As a general rule, we should think more about the fit than the fashion of our clothing. Many designers create wonderful clothing. But while some styles will look fantastic on each of us, many others will not. Our clothing should enhance our natural physique. Many women incorrectly assume that the more expensive the clothing, the better the fit. This is not necessarily true. If the fit doesn't suit their frames, they will have defeated their purpose. Then there are other women who get trapped by the "sales syndrome." If an item is on sale, no matter how improperly it may suit them, they buy it anyway. They compromise proper fit for a "bargain." They rationalize that because it's such a "good price," they couldn't "pass it up."

Sales are terrific. What woman doesn't enjoy getting a discounted price? However, whether your price range is budget, moderate, or couture, keep in mind, put fit first. Whether an item cost $50, $500, or $5,000, make sure it's suitable to your body and personality. Looking good is not only what you wear, but how well you wear it.

Many women copy each other's style of dressing. They imitate someone who is some inches taller or shorter, or who weighs several pounds more or less. Most often, the look they admired on another does not work for them. Each woman should consider what's best for her individual structure when choosing her garments. What's suitable for one, many not be suitable for another. Each should select her wardrobe based on the style, color, and fabric that looks and feels good on her.

COLORING YOUR WARDROBE

There are many theories on how to use color effectively when choosing your wardrobe. "Color analysts" claim to be able to determine what works best for each woman. It is quite true that certain shades will look nicer on your complexion than others, and will give you a radiant and dynamic glow, while others can give you a washed-out, drawn look. But, overall, women of color can successfully wear the vibrant red-orange-yellow group, as well as the placid blue-green-purple spectrum. You can basically wear any color you choose. However, if you especially like a certain shade, but feel that it is not flattering to you, choose an accessory (a scarf, jewelry, blouse), that is more suitable to your complexion and wear it close to your face. If you want to project a certain image at an important business or social event, your use of color is important. For example:

RED projects an aggressive, passionate or romantic image.

YELLOW or **ORANGE** will make you appear optimistic, cheerful, and warm.

GREEN will say you are a person who is calm, stable and in control.

NAVY BLUE gives an image of intellect, authority, and power.

PURPLE (especially when blended with gold accessories) suggests a regal, artistic, and wealthy nature.

PINK promotes a lovable, delicate, and compassionate aura.

BROWN lends a comfortable, natural, and earthy appearance.

BLACK shows mystery, sensuality, and sophistication.

WHITE relates innocence, cleanliness, and purity.

A combination of **BLACK** and **WHITE** projects a disciplined, stable, and serious image.

Take the time to experiment with many different colors. See which ones brighten your face and your personality. To decide which color is most complimentary to your skin tone, wrap your head with a white towel (if your hair is dyed), stand against a white background, and wearing no makeup, drape various colored fabrics around your neckline and over your shoulders, to see which ones bring life to your face. Get together with some friends and have you own color analysis party. You will get the benefit of your friends' opinions as well as your own. Each of you can learn to wear your best colors, and intensify the beauty of your natural coloring.

Let your dressing reflect prosperity and wealth. The "expensive" look need not cost a lot of money. The secret of power dressing is to pay twice as much, but purchase half as many. To the well-dressed woman, quality is more important than quantity. Don't be "penny-wise and pound-foolish." You will be better off financially because:

1. You'll get more pleasure from your garments because better clothes always stay in style longer.

2. Quality always lasts twice as long; therefore, you'll get twice the wear as you would from an inferior product.

3. You'll get better service and advice from a sales person selling a $100 dress than from one selling a $50 dress.

Make sure your appearance tells the world, "Here is a woman who is special. She is beautiful and respectful. She should be treated that way."

4
Sister to Sistuh

4

Sister to Sistuh

Is a hyacinth more beautiful than a lily, or a carnation lovelier than a tulip? Who can be the judge of which is more beautiful?

Just as flowers ray in their beauty, so do women. All are beautiful, whether of Caucasian, Asian, Hispanic, Indian, or African descent. There is no set standard for flowers, and there should be none for women. People may have individual preferences, but to compare one type of beauty to another is totally false. Comparison is an ugly practice. Once you compare, a standard is set. Expecting all nations to meet one standard is both destructive and harmful.

Is a yellow rose more valuable than a red rose, or a white more than a pink?

African American women are like roses. They are created in many shades. Who has the right to place value on the varying complexions?

Due to fictitious standards African American women have suffered when their beauty and social acceptability has been dependent on their features and color.

Although this has been going on for two hundred years, this disgraceful condition still affects many African Americans today, no matter how silent they may be about it. For, they themselves have adopted a complexion standard within their own race.

The only way to erase this type of false programming is to acknowledge it, analyze it, and disregard it. If you have a wound on your foot and do not treat it, doesn't the affliction become widespread? If you bandage it, cover it up, because you are ashamed of "John" seeing it, won't the disease continue to fester, until you eventually lose your foot? But if the wound is exposed and properly treated, so what if "John" saw it? Wouldn't it be better if he saw it, and it healed?

Instead of Blacks silently belittling each other, shouldn't we openly attempt to "walk a mile in each other's shoes" and try to understand that we are all victims of this so-called standard? To my darker-skinned sisters, realize that it is no compliment to be told, "At least you're pure and not confused." And to my lighter-skinned sisters, acknowledge that it is no blessing to be told, "At least you're not too dark and can be accepted a little better."

How tragically dehumanizing for another person or race to set standards for others to live by. Which human being has a right to brainwash another? Who has the right to decide which of God's creations is acceptable over others? Can the clay look at the potter and say you are not molding me correctly? Or can man look at his Maker and say you are not forming me right? No one has the right to criticize any of God's creations. The Creator has blessed each of us with our unique and individual features. Is man, therefore, greater than his Creator, to elect himself an authority on which of God's creations is ideal and which is not? People's behavior can be ugly, but their forms are all beautiful, no matter how varied, they are all of equal value.

Women of color must take the initiative to respect and appreciate each other in spite of our differences. Many of us may feel that we are not affected by this prejudice. But if we happen to be in certain places, at the wrong time, in this country, we are not welcomed. Until each and every black woman, man, and child can walk and dwell in any corner of the United States, peacefully and safely, we are all affected, either directly or indirectly, regardless of who we are. Let us try to understand each other's experience and free ourselves from this psychological bondage.

There is a special tie between sisters of color when dealing with issues on a one-to-one basis. But when a third force comes into play-- be it a man, money, or a certain position-- some women begin to discredit each other's worth, sensing competition. Let us acknowledge right now that there is no "real" competition in life. It's all an illusion, for "what is truly yours, cannot be taken away." *Competing* is one of life's three self-defeating C's. The other two are *comparing* and *copying*. These are misleading values that our society encourages. Instead of thinking "I have to keep up with the Joneses," or "I have to look and be better than Jane Doe," shouldn't we each be thinking "I must be the best that I can be"? If we would all concentrate on being our best individual selves, we would have no time to compare, copy, or compete with our own sisters, brothers, or persons from any other ethnic group. We would strive to help instead of hinder each other.

The plain truth is, we are all passengers on this oversized boat called Earth. And whether we sink or survive depends on how well we can paddle together. If one of us should fall overboard, who will rescue her? If all are selfish, she will drown. However, if there is a spirit of community, one of our crew members will gladly rescue our sibling. Our Divine Creator is the only captain of this ship. No one else on Earth has the right to determine our fate.

One of the most degrading remarks a person of another race can make to an African American is, "to me you're not Black, you are different." However well-intended, this is a very awkward compliment. These people may genuinely mean well, but this is not praise. When someone tells us this, what they are actually saying is, "because you're intelligent, well-spoken, beautiful, or successful, you can't be of the Black race." Would a Black woman tell a person of another race, "to me you are not of your racial background, you are so different?" Would people of other races accept such a remark as a compliment, no matter how well-meant? Why should any Black person accept this statement?

If any African American takes statements of this nature as compliments, she is doing both her self and her race a great disservice. Although innocently shared, and honestly meant, it should be corrected. Simply, in a polite manner, thank the person for the kind effort, but let them know that you are very much Black, just one of the very many who do not fit the stereotypical image portrayed about African Americans. This is in no way meant to belittle well-meaning peers, but to help to educate them. If you are to be true friends, you must be able to communicate openly with each other, or else the friendship or acquaintance will be built on sheer hypocrisy. As a true friend, they will be grateful to you for pointing this out, because they probably don't understand the impact of negative statements such as these. They too are victims of a psychological conditioning that has been mapped out by their forefathers. All of their lives they have been led to believe, either silently or openly, that being the offspring of the governing body in America, assures them a psychological edge over the other ethnic groups. And if their beliefs have not been corrected, then being exposed to Blacks who are just as beautiful, intelligent, articulate, or successful as they are, can and does throw their thinking off its superficially programmed path. In other words, while they have been falsely conditioned to believe they are "better than," the majority of Blacks have been subliminally programmed to believe that they are "less than." The universal truth is, no race or individual is superior to another. The beauty of this truth lies within the power of the human mind. No particular race has better brains than another; their success depends on discipline and purpose. If we would only learn to effectively use the magic of our *intuitive thinking,* struggling for equality would be an issue of the past.

We must become aware of our obstacles and develop plans to overcome them. We are strong, intelligent and capable beings. We have achieved much, but still need to accomplish much more. Until African Americans, individually and collectively, learn how to rely on self, think for self, and do for self, and share this knowledge with friends, children and communities, we will always be at the dictates of a governing body outside of our ethnic group. It's that simple. The Divine Creator has given all humans the same gift of *free will.* We all house it in our body temples. We are all the same, equal in the eyes of our Creator, who admonished from

the very beginning, *"Let us make man in our own image."*
Somewhere along the line one group decided to cruelly use
this powerful gift of the mind to outwit others. One group
took control over unsuspecting, peaceful-thinking groups.

All races at some point, throughout time, have been
subdued by another, but they all eventually overcame their
oppressors. The Hebrews were subjugated by the Egyptians,
the Jews by the Germans, and the Koreans by the Japanese.
Their freedom came by collectively discovering how to use
the power of their minds to believe in themselves, unite with
their siblings, and take hold of their own destinies.

For this guidance, the Hebrews had Moses, the Indians
had Gandhi, and the Chinese had Confucius. These groups to
this day are strongly united by brotherly appreciation.
Blacks in America had a fine example in Martin Luther King,
Jr. Unfortunately, we are still somewhat very scattered,
because we tend to be an ego oriented group. Once we've
reached a certain level of status, we are quick to separate
ourselves from a fellow brother or sister who is still trying
to find his or her way along the path. We have this need to
prove that we, too, are "better than" our very own brother
or sister. So much unnecessary time is spent trying to prove
that we look, dress, think, act, buy, or drive better than, our
fellow Black siblings. Have you ever encountered any other
ethnic group who will render a deaf ear to the cries of their
siblings? They kindly lend a helping hand to each other,
whether in the form of information, inspiration, love,

finances, respect, appreciation, or just simple acknowledgment. Why is it that we of Black descent do not take a more active role in promoting each other's ideas, businesses, trades or endeavors? If we do not think enough of ourselves to patronize each other, how can we expect other ethnic groups to do so? This is not in any way implying that we should confine ourselves, our friendships, relationships, or spending power, to our ethnic group; no, it's important to interact, learn, and grow with other cultures, but let us not neglect the very rich and beautiful culture that is our very own.

Behind the masks we wear-- Blacks, Whites, Asians, Indians, and Hispanics-- we are all the same deep within. We are all human beings trying to make it in this world; all are striving to be fulfilled in our friendships and relationships, and to earn enough money to live without worry. There is no intrinsic difference between people. We vary in our upbringing, exposure to situations, and basic guidance. It is unfortunate that because of ignorance of divine love, human beings have foolishly divided themselves by their outer shells.

It is truly beyond any reasonable comprehension, that people can actually dislike each other, simply because of the color of their skins. If human beings could come to the realization that we are all the same beyond these flesh temples, and embrace each other for who we are, instead of how we look, our lives on this planet would be so much more peaceful.

What's even more distasteful is that Black women in particular, are disrespected more than any other ethnic group in the United States. How ridiculous of anyone to discriminate against a certain sector of the population, simply because the Creator has colored their skins with various shades of beautiful brown and because they are female.

Although we cannot prevent other ethnic groups from throwing discriminating remarks at us, we can, however, love, respect, and appreciate ourselves to the extent where such statements would have no impact.

Everyone is entitled to his or her opinions. We can't stop people from prejudging. Although it may not be right, it is done. Each of us at, some point or another, is also guilty of prejudging other human beings. Therefore, we shouldn't condemn others for their prejudices, but we don't have to accept or believe them either. We must all try to live harmoniously with each other. But if Blacks do not care for each other, who will care for us? This doesn't mean we must tolerate every Black person, just because they happen to be Black. By all means, no. If anyone causes you discomfort or harm, you should remove yourself from that person's reach. However, let's spread some compassion towards each other as a whole.

If we would each take the responsibility to simply brighten up the little corner in which we live, that would be enough to increase respect towards African Americans in our society. If each of us would just influence five people in our lifetime, and they in turn then influenced five more, and so on, this would be a great awakening. A positive vibration would be created, an electrical current, spreading like wildfire, from one sister to another.

We could all see our ideas materialize and our dreams achieved. It would be a better world for ourselves and for future generations.

AFFIRMING OUR YOUTHS AND COMMUNITIES

Our ancestors were brought here against their wills. They were enslaved, and cruelly mistreated. But that is the past. We are, now, the great, great grandchildren of slavery. For our generation, this is the only homeland we know. It is important to know where we have been, but even more important, to know where we are going. We should grow out of our psychological slavery. We must start looking forward. Let us make this place as comfortable as we can for ourselves, our children, and for our children's children. Yesterday is gone. Our focus should be on today. What can we do now to rectify the situation of Blacks in today's world?

People don't want to hear about culture when they are hungry. Our youths need to be nourished today. One of our chief problems is scarcity-- Lack of food, improper housing, inadequate education. Scarcity and want deprives the mind of functional thought. It reduces people to the level of beasts. It leads to destruction and hate. It is the cause of many of our economic, social, psychological, physical, and political problems. If a man is full, he will not harm another in order to gain, because he already has. He will not think of shooting his own brother, or of pushing drugs for a "quick dollar." America is a very competitive country. We have been programmed to believe that our rise, fall, or survival depends on how well we can skillfully, or cunningly out-do each other. But Blacks must learn to think collectively. We must exercise a little tolerance and compassion towards each other.

Materialism plays a very important part in the Black awareness. If a man is without shelter, or a woman cannot pay her bills, how can they listen and pass on information towards the healing of a race? How is the hungry child to learn? How can the distraught personality function? What our Black sisters, brothers, and youths need is to know that they do matter.

Our Black youths are drowning in their neighborhoods. They are dying for an image. Limited exposure has led them to anger, frustration, and aggression. This is one reason why Black youths of today are entertained by guns. Guns give them a feeling of power. For instance, a young Black boy from an underprivileged background sees designer coats, jeans, and all-star sneakers being promoted as the "in thing." Being from the ghetto, how is he to afford this image? His gun now becomes his guarantee for getting "in." This is all very ugly. It has gotten way out of hand. And it needs to stop now.

As we all know, America is nourished by scandal. The media can be very damaging. What may be entertaining to a small group, can be discrediting to an entire race of people. If the media would stop playing up all the negative issues, some of this violence would cease to exist. The spirit is being taken out of the Black youths today. If the mass population does not accept them, how are they to function? We definitely cannot or should not separate ourselves from the mass population, but shouldn't we have Black businesses in Black neighborhoods? Can't we see that money is power, and create economic associations within our own communities? Blacks have earning power here, particularly those who are successful athletes. An effort should be made to bring these role models together with underprivileged youths.

Sisters, since we are the mothers of our nation, shouldn't we nurture what we've given birth to? Our youths are crying for help. There are too many children out there who need to be properly guided, cherished, and nurtured. This is a major challenge, but we have to start somewhere. We may not be able to guide the older ones, but we can start by training the younger ones for the future. To quote a term from the Bible, *"Train up a child in the way he should go, and when he is old, he will not depart from it."*

Today we need a total awareness, both from the educated and non-educated classes, to reverse the downfall of the Black race. Separating ourselves based on our skin complexions is ugly. We are all connected. One sector of the population, directly or indirectly, affects the other sectors. The varying shades of our melanic skins don't matter; the main issue is our behavior patterns. We must come together and find effective solutions. The mind furnishes solutions to all problems. Instead of looking on the outside for change, waiting to "get a break," or hoping for things to get better for Blacks, the effort has to come from within the Black Community. The matter at hand is:

1. *What steps must we take to* get Blacks to stop destroying, betraying, and competing with each other?

2. *What steps must we take to* develop brotherhood associations, throughout the United States, in order to reach underprivileged Blacks, and encourage their participation in trade and institutional training?

3. *What steps must we take to* replace the outrageous, ruthless, and self-destructive behavior of many Blacks?

4. *What steps must we take to* stop the killing, robbing, and beating, of Blacks, by Blacks and other ethnic groups?

5. *What steps must we take to* replace hunger,

homelessness, and illiteracy, with proper food, shelter, and education for the underprivileged?

6. *What steps must we take to* have a Black-owned national television station?

7. *What steps must we take to* protect our children from abuse, and ensure proper teaching in the classrooms?

8. *What steps must we take to* get Blacks to participate in each other's trades and businesses?

9. *What steps must we take to* create books, schools, and institutions, to develop the *intuitive thinking* of Blacks?

10. *What steps must we take to* ensure that all of the above is built on a solid foundation that will last throughout our lifetime and future generations?

These issues need to be addressed by collective effort. We must all champion this cause. When Blacks have a sense of community, racial slurs and expressions by other ethnic groups will be meaningless and our self-worth will remain unshaken. *A wire standing alone is easily bent, but many wires bound together, into a cable, is not easily broken.*

5
"Know Thyself"

5

"Know Thyself"

We have come a long way. We were first torn from the womb of our motherland, brought to this country to be a-bused, mocked, and shunned. Then we were stripped of our dignity, pride, and self-respect, and forced to accept a new homeland.

That was yesterday; today we have journeyed far beyond the chains of bondage, laws of segregation, and denial of education. We have become teachers, lawyers, and psy-chologists. By now we should realize that we are no longer helpless.

But we still have a far way to go. Everyday millions of us complain about how miserable, helpless, and worried we feel. We are glad the past is over, yet we are not enjoying the present and we are fearful of the unknown future. Life is spent striving to "become someone." Someone happy, someone wealthy, someone famous, or someone "anyone," other than the "one" we presently are. We are always wishing for a better, a different, or a new life. Precious time is spent yearning and hoping, instead of embracing and enjoying. This is a tragic waste because we only have one life. A life sandwiched by two pieces of paper: a *birth certificate* when we enter; and a *death certificate* when we pass on.

The span between these two documents is limited. We can't change that fact; we can change our outlook. We can create a new awareness to improve our lives and enjoy our special allotted time on the planet. We can erase old thinking of fear, despondency, and loneliness, and replace it with new feelings of comfort, joy, and love.

Unhealthy dispositions cannot supply us with enjoyable lives. We can't celebrate life if we're always asking, "When will I be happy?", "What is my purpose in life?" or "Where is my slice of the pie?" Nor can we postpone life: "I'll be happy *after* I become successful, famous, rich, married, thin, promoted, or any other *afters* that we treasure. When we eventually accomplish our goals, and still have not found happiness, we are puzzled. Like *tomorrow, after* never comes. The Time to enjoy our lives is in the *here and now* of today, not in the uncertain *then and there* of tomorrow.

It is quite understandable that the majority of Black women are easily frustrated, doubtful, and insecure. We have been one of the least respected sectors of the American population. Not only have we experienced racial prejudices for being black, but we suffer sexual discrimination for being female. The negative images of Blacks, portrayed by the media, are a major contributor to our feelings of des-pondency and hopelessness. We have become so accustomed to news of crimes, drugs, diseases, and financial scarcity, that our minds have become subconsciously programmed to expect the worst. This is the type of con-ditioning that has formed pessimistic and unhealthy attitudes for too large a majority of African Americans.

As deplorable as this may be, it happens on a daily basis. There is no point in being annoyed or resentful. It won't help. The only way to better our situation is to empower ourselves, our children, and our communities.

This empowerment begins with the greatest love of all--self-love. Not a selfish love, but a "self-ful" love. A love that is full of self-appreciation, self-approval, and self-acceptance. Only when we take responsibility for ourselves, and cultivate positive self-images regardless of the opinions of others, can we create effective and lasting changes.

To find the *key* to optimistic and healthy attitudes, we must venture beyond our physical boundaries, beyond the walls of set standards, confinement, and limited controlled knowledge, and "open the door" to our *intuitive thinking*. We can then eliminate our fears, and reprogram our minds to achieve our individual desires.

ELIMINATING OUR FEARS

The purpose of *intuitive thinking* is to find solutions to our problems. But we must just allow it to work for us. We were never taught in school how to use our greater mind-- only our physical, conscious mind. We learned our ABCs, reading, writing, and arithmetic, but not the power of *intuitive thinking*.

Fear is a major barrier to *intuitive thinking*. It enters practically every corner of our lives. We are fearful of poverty, loneliness, other people's opinions, ill-health, old age, death, and life after death. But, most importantly, we are fearful of ourselves. We are afraid to manage our own thinking, our own feelings, and our own lives. Fear of self stems from lack of belief in our own abilities. This causes doubt, worry, and anxiety.

Everyday thousands of us come up with creative ideas. These ideas are interesting and important. But we ignore them. If we heard the same ideas from others, we would have readily accepted them. We wrongly *underestimate* the value of our own thinking, while we falsely *overestimate* the thinking of others.

Most people have more respect for others than they do for themselves. They wish they were in someone else's body, job, or lifestyle. This explains why so many people surrender to the dictates of others. We frequently allow others to run our lives because we are afraid of losing that person's love. We sacrifice our own feelings.

This type of existence creates psychological, as well as physical, disharmony. We shy away from making our own decisions because we are too concerned about what other people may think. We allow these self-limiting fears to control how we govern ourselves. This destroys our creativity, curiosity, and spontaneity. It prevents us from getting where we want to go, having the kind of fun we want to have, and doing the things we want to do.

Although most people are fearful because they believe they "are not good enough," there are many who are afraid of being seen as "better than." They believe that if they excel at what they do, people may resent them; or if they express their creative ideas, others may think they are "showing off." Some people are contemptuous of anyone who dares to be original. It's easy for people to criticize. Anyone is capable of doing that. But to come up with effective solutions is another story. If you feel you have to deny your creativity to be accepted, it's time to change the company you keep.

We must choose friends and associates who respect our thinking, those who can enhance our growth, and with whom we can exchange stimulating ideas.

To free ourselves to think intuitively, we must get rid of our imagined fears. Fear is faith in reverse. Faith is positive belief; fear is negative.

The only way to overcome most fears is to do exactly what you are afraid of. If you are afraid of meeting new people, deliberately force yourself to do so. In all social settings, practice being the first to introduce yourself to others. Give yourself pep talks, like the following, before making your approach: "I admit this usually scares me, but I'm going to do it. I may not enjoy this at first because I'm not conditioned to do so, but I'm going to start right now." Practice doing this until you learn to be at ease when meeting people.

If you are fearful of asking questions, ask them anyway. No question is ever "stupid." Asking questions is the only way to get answers. If you are afraid of applying for a certain position, research the field and gather information on the subject. If you are afraid of public speaking, practice in front of friends or join a toast masters club. If you are fearful of your appearance, get a professional beauty make-over. The point is, to conquer whatever is hindering you from fully being yourself.

Start now; today. Whenever you go to a restaurant, a department store, or anyplace where you have to pay money to be waited on, decide to be your true self. When in a restaurant, do not order something just because others do. Order what you really want to have. If the waiter insists that you try "the special of the day," but you are not certain that you would like to, then don't. Most of the time, they are instructed to "move" the daily specials, either because they have too much on hand, or it yields a good profit for the restaurant. Simply smile, thank the waiter for his suggestion, and place an order of your own choice. When in clothing stores, do not let sales people "push" items on you. They work for commission and are often required to meet a daily quota. You should be the one to decide exactly what looks good on you. You should choose clothing which enhances your individual physique based on the style, material, and color. If you feel pressured, politely, yet firmly, let the salesperson know that you'd like to be left alone to make up your own mind on what is best for you. If you do not feel like making a purchase, then don't. Always remember, you're not obligated to do so, just because the salesperson has spent time with you.

The woman who acknowledges herself as the manager of her own destiny is a successful person. She directs her own actions and supervises her own life. She takes responsibility for all of her successes, as well as for her setbacks. She does not blame "other people," "hard times," or "bad luck" for her circumstances.

Each of us must embrace the responsibility for both the good and bad in our lives. Many of us are quick to blame others when we are not doing well at work, in relationships, or when others get ahead of us. It is very easy to point a finger at someone else, but this will not make us any better. The sooner we each take hold of our own lives, the sooner we can improve things.

When negative thoughts become visitors in our minds, we must question why we are thinking in that manner. Our minds absorb and react to whatever we put into them. That is why it is so important for us to fear nothing. For, whatever we fear we will attract to us. We must find positive images to replace all fears. Negative thoughts can come from many sources, including other people. By developing our intuitive minds, we can become aware of these thoughts, and choose to block them out. Whenever fear enters, we must think: "I am free of all fear that exists now and in the future."

Anything our minds can believe, we can achieve. Please read this once again: Anything our minds can believe, we can achieve.

If we *really deeply* believe we will have financial success, then we shall.

If we *really deeply* believe we will have fulfilling love, then we shall.

If we *really deeply* believe we will have peace of mind, then we shall.

Whatever our minds can believe, we can achieve. This is the well-guarded Conceive, Believe, Achieve (CBA) secret, known to the privileged few, passed down through many ages, but not taught in any classroom. Do not take it lightly. Realize the power in this truth: If we can *conceive* the thought in our minds, and can *believe* it with all of our hearts, then we can surely *achieve* it in our lives. All solutions are within us, we need not look outside. We only need to unfold our *intuitive thinking,* and let it work for us; for *"greater is that which is in us, than that which is in the world."*

We must not confuse *wishing* with *believing.* A *wish* is of the surface, conscious mind; it merely entertains us, with no true power to manifest itself. A *belief* stems from the very depth of our *intuitive thinking,* and actually brings about the changes that occur in our lives.

Succeeding in life doesn't always come easy. It takes a lot of persistence, perseverance, and courage. At times you'll feel as if it's hopeless to try. On some days you may not be able to see the "light at the end of the tunnel." On other days you'll be reduced to tears. But no matter how discouraging situations may become at times, *do not give up.* Success may not come overnight, but it does come, if you are determined to win. This is a given fact, *you will win.* If you keep knocking at a door, it is bound to open. The only way to lose, is to quit trying. "A winner never quits, and a quitter never wins," runs an old saying. This is true, and should help you to realize that there is nothing in this world that you cannot *achieve,* if you truly *believe* with all your heart.

People from all corners of the world have taken fervent interest in developing their *intuitive thinking;* From government officials, film stars, businessmen, professional athletes, career women, and top representatives of large corporations, to housewives, teachers, and students. They believe the power of *intuitive thinking* will give them the key to solving their social, business and personal problems. It will unlock the passage to creating their very own *victories.* The lonely will become loved, the poor will become rich, the sick will become well, the unappreciated will become well-respected, and the defeated will become winners.

This *key* to *intuitive thinking* involves a three-fold process. It is built upon the foundation of MEDITATION-*knowing* what you want; VISUALIZATION- *seeing* the image in your mind; and AFFIRMATION- *ordaining* through the spoken word.

To make this process work for you, you must peacefully accept that *"if you have faith as tiny as a mustard seed, nothing shall be impossible unto you."* Don't doubt it, just *know* that you deserve it. You must live your life with *expectation; expect* your mind to perform any task you ask it to. Once your mind gives you the solutions, *focus* on them, and make every *effort* to materialize them. You will have what you desire because *focus* plus *effort* equals *manifestation.* Give thanks and accept this powerful truth, *"for whatsoever thing you desire, pray as if you had already received it and you shall surely have it."*

THE THREE-FOLD PROCESS TO INTUITIVE THINKING

MEDITATION

Meditation is one of the most useful, oldest and simplest processes available to us. In some traditions, it is used for worship. In others, it is used as a method to achieve self-knowledge. In today's psychology, it is being used as a therapeutic method. Yet when most people hear the word meditation, they automatically think of some esoteric or intricate system. Our society has made it seem like some mystical discipline that is difficult to gain. Some people do practice complicated forms of meditation through various ritualized mantras and specialized breathing techniques; but meditation is only *a state of relaxed thinking.* And thinking is as natural to human beings as breathing, eating, and sleeping.

Meditation requires no force, struggle or strain. To meditate you don't need any special type of training, equipment, talent, experience, personality, or education. All you need is to be *your natural self,* to concentrate on what is going on inside of *you,* to become uninvolved with your outside surroundings for the moment. You need to simply become relaxed.

When we meditate, we are opening our conscious minds to our *intuitive thinking,* allowing ourselves to reach a level of tranquillity. This is a very peaceful state, where all confusion disappears. We are able to tune into our higher psychological selves, and can know the *how, why, what,* and *where* of everything.

Relaxation is very important to our well-being and to the achievement of our desires. When we relax, we can see and think clearly about exactly what we want in our lives. We are then able to follow through with visualization, and affirm our beliefs into reality. Meditation is also very beneficial to us physically, because when we are in a state of relaxation, there is no room for *anxiety, despondency* or *frustration*-- the three major causes of *dis-ease* in the human body.

When you first begin to meditate, choose a time where you will not be disturbed. You can meditate anywhere. It could be lying on your bed, sitting on the floor, soaking in your bathtub, or sitting under a tree. Just close your eyes and take a few deep breaths. Become peaceful, comfortable, and calm. Ask yourself anything you need to know. Some answers will come right away; others will take a little longer. Once you receive the answers to questions, do not act immediately. Either meditate a little deeper or pray for proper guidance, in order to be sure that the answer is ideal for you. There are many solutions to any one problem. With this type of programming, you are now exposed to the center of your intuition. You can listen to your inner voice-- the voice of all wisdom and understanding. *"Let those with ears, hear."*

At some point, scattered thoughts and feelings may start to emerge in your mind. This is because the more you rely on the intuitive mind, the more sensitive your awareness becomes to all existing vibrations. Don't try to fight these scattered thoughts. Just keep yourself centered on the object of your meditation with complete ease. If you do not extend any effort on them, they will eventually float away, because they have no active energy to exist on. Only your ego (your conscious thinking) is capable of giving them life through reaction. Therefore, relax your ego, and surrender it to your particular *victory* of the moment. Know that you *are*, and can *do,* and can *have* whatever you *desire;* that you stand at the doorway of your *higher self.* And through the persistent use of meditation, in conjunction with visualization and affirmation, you just have to *"knock and it shall be opened unto you."*

VISUALIZATION

Visualization is simply seeing what we want to happen before it actually does. It is the act of using our imagination to create scenes that we desire in our lives. We form pictures in our minds all the time when we daydream. By visualizing, we can tailor our daydreams to suit our specific wants. It could be anything-- a certain type of relationship, a desired situation, object, career, or goal. There is no limit to what we can create in our "mind's eye."

The following are three very easy and effective steps to creative visualization:

1. *Imagine the thing or situation you wish to manifest.* For example, if you desire a new place of residence, picture the house or apartment you'd like to have. Try to see it clearly. It may be unclear at first, but continue to relax and focus on your new place to live until the image becomes vivid.

2. *See the thing or image already existing in the most perfect way.* Picture yourself moving around in your new home. Walk through your rooms. Observe the colors, furnishings, and decorating style you've chosen. See yourself perfectly comfortable in your new dwelling. It is very important that you must see what you desire as *already* existing. Learn to adjust yourself to *feel it, sense it, see it,* and *accept it.*

3. *Give thanks.* Embrace your visualization with love. You must be persistent in order for this to materialize. Some desires may manifest instantly, while others may take quite some time. Continue with all your heart to *"seek and ye shall surely find."*

AFFIRMATION

An affirmation is any statement we say or think, either

positively or negatively. It is a declaration of acceptance. Whatever we accept about ourselves, we eventually become. Too often we continually make negative affirmations to ourselves, like, "Just the thought of it *makes me sick,*" or *"I hate* the way I look." These negative statements cause disharmony in our lives and hinder our growth. When we repeatedly affirm anything, it becomes impressed in our minds and, therefore, becomes capable of molding the thoughts that forms the situations in our lives.

The following easy technique should serve to help you achieve individual desires:

1. *Always affirm in the present tense.* You should never affirm in the future tense. For instance, you shouldn't say, "I will be happy," or "I will have peace of mind," but instead say, "I am now happy," or "I now am at peace with myself." The reason for this is that our minds are such obedient and efficient servants that if declarations are made in the *future* tense, they'll be *there,* and not *here* in the *present.*

2. *Always declare positive statements.* For example, don't say, "I am *not* sick or "I am *not* insecure," but instead say "I am perfectly healthy," or "I am secure."

3. *Always affirm with absolute intensity, conviction and feelings.* Don't just merely recite or mumble off your affirmations. Pour all your belief and desire into what you are stating. Don't be timid; be bold. Don't just hope, wish or want, but *demand, command, ordain*-- order your requests into present reality.

Many people have broken right through the door that was obstructing their inherent gift the first time they ever affirmed; not only did they *believe*, but they *knew* and *felt* the actuality of what they were ordaining. They didn't doubt or question it, they *evoked* and *accepted* it. Their minds were convinced of their spoken words.

The human mind is a beautiful instrument. It can be programmed for victories or defeats, wealth or poverty, love or hate, joy or misery. It is there to serve us. Always declare peace, perfection and prosperity. Open yourself to your *intuitive thinking* by requesting abundance and totality. Affirm exactly what you want and let it manifest through your unwavering power of concentration and belief. Continue to *"ask and it shall be given unto you."*

To affirm

    is to believe

to believe

    is to become

to become

    is to enjoy

to enjoy

    is the birthright of every individual on Earth.

REWRITING YOUR INDIVIDUAL SCRIPT
FOR AN ENJOYABLE LIFE

All human beings are born with the natural instinct to love. Somewhere along our life path, from childhood through adulthood, this instinct can be abused, mistreated, or unappreciated, by a parent, friend, lover, or stranger. This can make us cautious and distrustful of others-- and unappreciative of our own selves. In order to survive the hurt and pain we feel, consciously or subconsciously, we build protective coatings around our hearts.

Our hearts are the center of love. Love is life's natural medicine. Defending ourselves from it, has caused many of the unpleasantness in our lives-- the unpleasantness of unfulfilling relationships, insufficient understanding, lack of beauty, blocked creativity, or feelings of loneliness. We must dissolve our individual coatings of protection, and release the healing power of love, to nurture our individual minds, bodies, and spirits.

Life is a gigantic theatre. We are merely actors playing our various roles. At birth, we were handed scripts prepared by unsuitable playwrights; they have cast us into many unhappy scenes throughout our life experience. Nowhere in our individual scripts, is the universal truth written. The truth that we can rewrite, direct, and produce our own chosen performances, at any time we desire. This is the *"truth that will set us free."* We each have the ability to

95

dismiss any old belief, create new scenes, and cast any character to our liking.

We are able to do this with the most valuable gift we possess-- our minds. This precious gift is from our Divine Creator-- whether we wish to call Him God, Jehovah, or The Almighty. It is a most powerful gift of *free will*, that is always available to serve us.

As Black women within America, other people have set various standards regarding our characteristics, features, complexions, and thinking. However, such habits can have no personal effect on us, unless we ourselves choose to believe or accept these superficial standards.

Our minds are the only possessions we have total control over in life. The opinions of others cannot be absorbed into our thinking if we make conscious efforts to refuse them. Our minds are like our own personal safety deposit boxes. Only we possess the keys to either open or close them, and to decide which thoughts to put in or take out.

All Humans are striving to reach a state of contentment, but few are able to do so. This is because most people look for satisfaction in other people, places, and things. Outside escapes may supply temporary joy, but they have no lasting influence. True contentment can only come from within, when we learn to become at peace with ourselves.

It is very unfortunate that so many of us have to laugh to keep from crying. As the words of an old familiar song shares, "If there's a smile upon my face, it's only there trying to fool the public...tears of a clown." There have been too many sisters of color who have been slipping through life, unable to claim their birthright, unable to ignite the sparks of true joy.

As Black women today, we have the golden opportunity to take heed and create our own personalized productions. We can start at this very moment. Whatever limitations may have blocked our contentment, mustn't we venture around them? Can we afford to leave our fate in the hands of others?

Shouldn't we learn from the words of our elder brother, the Divine Nazarene, *"If thy right hand offend thee, cut it off, and cast it from thee: for it is profitable for thee that one of thy members should perish, and not that thy whole body should be cast in hell"*?

If anyone or anything causes us misery, pain, or harm, we must separate from that person or thing in order to have peace of mind. If a mate causes you distress-- emotional or physical-- you should sever the ties. It is better to be by yourself and happy, than to be with another and unhappy. If you dislike your job, select another field and resign. If excess weight is causing you discomfort, learn about proper nutrition, exercise, and get it off. There is a solution to every problem in life. But you must make the necessary effort.

The following is a sample script in which you actually write your own program for an enjoyable life. The outline includes some quotes from my first book, *The Fortune of Being Yourself.* It is designed to serve as a guideline for the beginning of your journey towards achievement and peace of mind.

TITLE:
RECLAIMING MYSELF

PLAYWRIGHT: _____
(your name)

ACT I – SCENE 1
NURTURING THE INTERIOR CHILD

Our personalities are formed by the situations, events and teachings we have accumulated during our life span. Although we can alter our thinking and improve ourselves at any point we choose, the foundation of our true selves was already formed by the age of ten. All other traits were later added to our primary bases, to build these complicated structures we now know as *our selves.*

In order to find out more about our true selves, and to rid ourselves of disharmonious programming, it is important to look within. We must contact and nurture the little stranger who we have hidden deep inside-- *the interior child*, the child who is lonely, lost and longing to be loved.

The way we handle situations depends on how we were treated as children. For example, if we were taught to only "speak when spoken to," our learned behavior causes us to be apprehensive of speaking our opinions, fearful of letting others know when we are uncomfortable. If we've been told we'd never amount to much, we've become very subservient to other people's needs, some times neglecting our own. Any extremity is unhealthy for our well-being. Even if we were overindulged, had our every demand catered to, if we weren't taught right from wrong, we grew up to expect the world to revolve around us, and are truly hurt when others do not meet our expectations.

Traumatic experiences can cause us to retreat within, shutting off very important parts of ourselves from life. Although many unpleasant memories may be hidden or blocked, we will subconsciously act them out because they were not corrected, just pushed aside.

Socrates admonished, "Know thyself." Most people take this to mean, "know thy conscious or surface self," without any regard to the intuitive self-- the true self, which is hidden deep within, waiting to be nurtured.

Let's take time to know the intuitive self, beginning with

the experiences of the little child you once were and still are within. We must *face, erase,* and *replace* any unhealthy memories.

This *scene* is designed to help you to rid yourself of any negative beliefs or insecurities caused from childhood experiences. These thoughts and feelings may be presently causing disharmony between your mind, body, and spirit. It is important to note, that with any deep cleansing, there is always tears and pain. Tears that wash away the old, to make room for the new, and pain that is not unhealthy, but truthful. Any unpleasant thing that happened to you as a child was not your fault; you should not be held responsible, or blame yourself, for any of these unfortunate experiences. Contentment will begin when you have spanned a bridge of positive memories, between your childhood and adulthood, to create a happy, wholesome self.

I NOW FACE IT:
Write the story of your childhood-- where you were born, the environment in which you were brought up, your family, home, school, etc. Write specific experiences which you remember that caused you to feel frightened, upset, angry, hated, alone, or embarrassed,...

I NOW ERASE IT:
Review your story of the little *you.* Find photos of yourself if possible. Study them carefully. Talk to that child. Find out how she's feeling, what makes her afraid, and

how you can help her. Comfort her; hug her. Let her know that you love her, and that she'll never be alone again. Tell her not to be afraid, not to believe any cruel or untrue thing that anyone may be saying to or about her. Let her know that she can trust you, that you were sent to guide her-- and that you will protect her, and make sure that no one can ever hurt her again...

I NOW REPLACE IT:

Relax and visualize that child being comforted by someone who cares for and loves her. Help her to create a happy childhood. *Know* that you have the ability to do so. Share the power of positive affirmations with your *interior child.* Help her to rewrite her story. This time, record only the good and positive images and experiences about this little girl and how happy she is...

ACT I – SCENE 2
DESIGNING MY PERSONAL PROFILE

Of all relationships, the most important one you will ever have is with yourself. You spend more time with yourself that you can ever spend with another. But how many people actually take time to get acquainted with their own selves? How many listen to, speak with, or even like themselves?

(page 16, THE FORTUNE OF BEING YOURSELF)

Write a detailed description of your basic mannerisms and preferences. For example, write about your favorite color, the way you dress, the type of books and music you like; the places, hobbies, pets, movies, or topics you enjoy...

The things I like most about myself are...

The things I dislike most about myself are...

I could correct these things if...

My affirmations to improve the way I feel about myself:

I am original, unique, and special. I am one of a kind, therefore, I am priceless.

I feel guided and protected in every way by divine powers.

I am now at peace with myself. I am confident, courageous, successful and bold.

(continue to create your own affirmations)

ACT I – SCENE 3

ACCENTUATING MY BEAUTIFUL ASSETS

...beauty publications and most television commercials dictate how the 'ideal' woman should look. The majority of women– who do not reflect these images– end up resenting

themselves and wishing they looked like someone else ...Let me share with you, right now, the most important beauty tip you will ever need to know: THE KEY TO BEING BEAUTIFUL IS TO ENJOY BEING YOURSELF. FOR YOUR BEAUTY IS AS INDIVIDUAL AS YOU ARE.

(*page 63, THE FORTUNE OF BEING YOURSELF*)

This *scene* is for you to develop a special admiration for your own beauty. Write at least six compliments for each of the following features. Don't be modest. As a matter of fact, let your ego have fun emphasizing your beautiful assets...

SKIN   HAIR   NOSE
    LIPS   SMILE   TEETH
EYES   NAILS   HANDS
    FEET   BODY   HEIGHT
WEIGHT   POSTURE   HYGIENE

ACT II – SCENE 1
FREEING MYSELF OF NEGATIVE COMPANY

One of the most emotionally draining situations to experience is lack of support from loved ones-- be they family members, friends, or lovers. We all grow at different paces in life. When you've accelerated past or outgrown a certain level of thinking, even some of the closest people in your life may have some difficulty understanding or accepting this.

They may unintentionally hold you back by discouraging your dreams. At times, they may do and say belittling things which cause you emotional hurt, confusion, and insecurity.

The sad truth is that most people give up their innermost dreams when faced with disapproval from a loved one. They abandon their true hopes of flying to the heights of success, and instead flutter in mediocrity, all because of ill-gotten advice.

Some of these loved ones genuinely mean well, but are just afraid of being left behind. However, it is an unfortunate fact that there are some who are simply envious and selfish. Accepting advice from people who don't understand you is like taking a beautifully designed couture dress to be altered by a 'five and dime' seamstress. You are too important to be tailored by a five and dime adviser.

You must be true to yourself. Respect your feelings. Firmly, but politely assure these people, that you do love them and will always be there for them, but that they will have to respect the fact that *you* know what's best for you.

Explain to them that you are no longer a caterpillar hibernating in its cocoon, that you have become a brilliantly-colored butterfly about to spread her wings. Let them know that it would make you happy if they would come fly with you, but you will no longer be enclosed.

Make a list of all the people who cause you discomfort, and the reasons why. After you've compiled your list, review and discuss it with the people or person accordingly. Let them know how much this affects you, and try to really work things out. However, if they are still unwilling to grant you the respect you deserve, don't react negatively; instead realize the plain truth, that *you can't change others, but you can certainly direct yourself.* Remain focused on your goals. Don't compromise. You can continue to be polite, loving and friendly, but do not share your dreams with them; move out of their reach.

My affirmations for freeing myself of negative company:

It's unfortunate that_____ doesn't understand my desires. I love him/her anyway, but I have to move on.

I know that_____ loves and means me well, but I have to be true to my dreams, and I hope that he/she will grow to understand someday.

Although_____ has hurt me, I hold no anger towards him/her. I forgive him/her and wish him/her well in his/her own circle.

I now choose friends and associates who respect my thinking, who I can exchange stimulating ideas with, and who enhance my growth.

ACT II – SCENE 2
LABORING WITH LOVE

For a woman, there are three ways to get money. You can inherit it, marry it or work for it...let's discuss the majority of women – those who work for their daily bread. Your career occupies a large part of your life. It is very important to choose one you will enjoy. Too many people look back on their career choice and think, "I could have been." They are functioning in their careers, but they are not happy. Many doctors want to be actors, and many actors want to be doctors. Many lawyers want to be teachers, and many teachers want to be lawyers...Surveys show that 80 out of every 100 people hate the work they are doing.

(page 89, THE FORTUNE OF BEING YOURSELF)

Money doesn't come to you without any effort. It is an exchange for services rendered to others. It is earned by the combination of *focus* and *labor.* You must focus on exactly what you intend to give in exchange for money, and you must labor to manifest your focus.

Write a description of your perfect day at work. Create a scenery that is ideal for you. Observe and record your surroundings, your ex-pressions, and your feelings. What are you doing, what are you wearing, and who are you interacting with? Are things running smoothly? Take into consideration the following points when describing your ideal labor of love:

1. Why do I like it?
2. What do I need from it?
3. What do I want from it?
4. How can I help others by it?
5. How can it make me a better person?
6. I have been unable to pursue my ideal career because...
7. The skills I need to be qualified for this work are...
8. I can obtain these skills if...
9. The skills I already have which qualify me for this work are...
10. I now choose to pursue my ideal career in the following ways...

ACT III – SCENE 1
PLANNING MY PURPOSE IN LIFE

Many people spend their lives wishing to achieve their dreams, yet failing to properly plan, organize, and carry out their desires. They drift aimlessly along, taking each day as it comes, accepting what is dished out to them. They have made no plans for living. They have not decided what their purpose in life is. They merely wish themselves to do better, or they wish they were in better surroundings. Or most common of all, "I wish I had a million dollars." ...You cannot wish yourself into an ideal relationship or a better body. You can, however, create goals, make plans and get to work on them.   *Write down on paper what you expect to achieve. The time to start is now.*

(*page 24, THE FORTUNE OF BEING YOURSELF*)

My personal plan for the *next month* is:
Three months:
Six months:

My personal plan for the *next year* is:
Three years:
Five years:
Ten years:

My personal plan for *life* is:

ACT III – SCENE 2
CREATING MY PERFECT LIFESTYLE

Write a short story, describing the ideal life you want for yourself. Write in the present tense; be specific. Live it as you record it.   Let your imagination run wild.   Don't limit yourself to what you think may or may not be possible. Become uninhibited and walk through it with total freedom. Use the following three categories to assist you: people, places, and things.

<u>People</u> – whom do you socialize with, work with, have fun with, travel with?   What types of people are a part of

your surroundings – actors, authors, athletes; bankers, bakers, businessmen? What are the different age groups; the ethnic, social, political, educational, economic or religious backgrounds?

Places – Where do you live? In a Hollywood mansion, a New York penthouse, a London flat, a Swiss chalet, a Texas farm, or a simple cozy country home? Where do you vacation, work, shop, dine, relax; the continents, the countries, the islands; the hotels, resorts, boutiques, stores, restaurants?

Things – What do you own? Stocks, bonds, clothing, jewelry, cars, yachts, planes, Picassos, pets? What do you like to do? The kind of work, the types of hobbies, entertainment, recreations? Do you dance, design, discover; are you a secretary, scientist, sculptor?

As you create your ideal lifestyle, remember not to hinder your thoughts in any way. Write as if you had all the freedom, money, power, and skills necessary to live this perfect fantasy.

After you have finished composing your soul-searching fantasy, you'll realize that some of the people, places, and things may be much more meaningful to you than others. This part of the *scene* is to help you define the most important priorities for achieving your desired lifestyle.

By breaking down the elements, you'll gain a clearer picture of your indispensable desires. You'll be able to direct your creative energies towards turning your fantasy into reality.

Arrange your fantasy into three divisions as follows:
Division 1: I MUST HAVE
Division 2: I WANT, BUT DON'T REALLY NEED
Division 3: I CAN ACTUALLY DO WITHOUT

ACT III – SCENE 3
LIVING MY LIFE TO THE FULLEST, TODAY

People have very little respect for time. No one knows what their life expectancy is. Every day thousands of people die in this world. Life is too short to be wasted. Death is something natural that we all must eventually face. People don't like to discuss this, and that's understandable. But, it isn't a 'bad' thing. It is as important a characteristic of nature as birth is. What's unfortunate is that most of the thousands of people who will die today never truly enjoyed the voyage.

(page 29, THE FORTUNE OF BEING YOURSELF)

At this point, you have the opportunity to take charge of your life. Just for this moment, pretend that this is your last day on Earth, and you want to enjoy each moment to the fullest. Write a description of how you'd spend this important day, the people you'd get in touch with-- a long lost friend perhaps, or maybe you'd make amends with someone for a misunderstanding you had. What activities would you enjoy? How would you pamper yourself? Is there someone you'd like to say "thank you" to, but haven't bothered to do?

If today was my last day on Earth, I would...

When you have completed writing your plan for living today, review your list and select the things you can actually do for yourself today-- and do them. Your life is too important to put off for *tomorrow,* it can make you happy *today.*

EPILOGUE

There is nothing better for a man, than he should
eat and drink, and that he should make his soul enjoy
good in his labour.
For God giveth to a man that is good in his sight
wisdom, and knowledge, and joy...
Ecclesiastes 2:24,26

111

6
That Magic Touch

6
That Magic Touch

...if two lie together, then they have heat:
but how can one be warm alone?
Ecclesiastes 4:11

When a woman is in love, her entire system becomes alert. She reaches peaks she otherwise never would have reached. Love nourishes her. No other experience is so deep and pleasing.

When love becomes a part of her, her entire being is blissful. Her work, her walk, her posture, and her activities, all carry the expression of her joy. She is consumed with extraordinary feelings of bright sun-filled mornings and relaxing afternoons. To her, the miracle of Spring is always present. The dizzy power of love enriches her with a sense of self-dignity.

At her very center-- her interior-- she possesses the sun, the moon, and the universe. She enjoys being in love. She feels total. She lives for love.

THE LANGUAGE DIFFERENCE BETWEEN MEN AND WOMEN IN RELATIONSHIPS

Men and women do not speak the same language in relationships. Men are more physical; women are more emotional.

To fully understand this reality, let us take a look at two different explanations-- one from Western psychologists, and the other from Eastern philosophers:

Western psychologists explain that these behavior patterns are a result of social conditioning in childhood. Men and women are taught to assume their masculine (physical), and feminine (emotional) roles respectively. As little boys, men were taught to be strong, and not show emotions. They were scolded for any sensitivity or tears-- or ridiculed as "sissys." They were expected to mature into courageous, firm, and admired men.

Women, as little girls, were told to always act "ladylike," (submissive), and look pretty. They were comforted and nurtured when they cried. They were expected to grow up to become feminine women who would be taken care of by "Prince Charming."

These programmed teachings have resulted in women being more open to emotions, and men being more closed to emotions.

Eastern philosophers share that men and women are governed by different spiritual energies. The female energy represents *love and devotion,* also known as *Bhakti Yoga.* The male energy represents *meditation and wisdom*, also known as *Gyana Yoga.* In love, another is desired. In meditation, another is not necessary. Being alone, without feeling lonely, comes more naturally to those governed by the male energy, while it's very difficult for the entities ruled by the female energy to feel so independent. It runs against their natural instincts. While men can achieve contentment through *deep thinking,* women do so through *deep feeling.* It is virtually impossible for women to gain complete harmony without some form of love-- whether that be love of a man, a child, a friend, a cause, a career, a pet, or a spiritual ideal. The list is endless, but she must love. She must feel wanted, must feel needed, must feel nurturing, in order to experience inner peace.

Although both theories are so very different, they both

agree that in relationships, men are more physical and women are more emotional. This does not make one sex more capable than the other. This is not an issue of equality vs. inequality. These are just some basic differences, that were either designed by nature or conditioned by society. It is a fact that men and women display different behavioral patterns in relationships.

I have often wondered why women of all ages, colors, and shapes, from varying intellectual, financial, and social backgrounds, share emotional behavior-- behavior which directs their actions in relationships.

This is not to imply that men do not *feel and love deeply,* or that women are not *deep-thinking and wise.* There are varying degrees of female behavior in all men, and male behavior in all women. Therefore, you'll find many men who are compassionate, loving, and sensitive, and many women who are detached, reclusive, and stoic. Many men and women share a combination of all the above characteristics. But, overall, it is indisputable that while women *feel more emotionally,* men *think more physically.*

THE DEPTH OF LOVING RELATIONSHIPS

Relationships can be beautiful, caring, and loving, but they can also become destructive, harmful, and ugly.

Relationships are complicated because they involve two individual, separate minds. Success depends on both people. We are no longer in our own individual worlds. We have merged with another human being and a new world; a new experience now exists.

We are never the same during or after any relationship. We begin by forming our relationships, then, along the way, our relationships form us. At the onset, only our exteriors meet. We reserve our interiors from each other. Then, when we progress deeper, closer, and become more intimate, eventually our interiors start to merge.

When two interiors blend, there is a new creation. The combination of hydrogen and oxygen, forms a new substance-- water. Hydrogen and oxygen are each useful separately, but they cannot quench thirst. It is the union, the water, that brings forth deep love to fulfill the thirst in many lives.

When two exteriors come together, it is only an acquaintance. We have not reached deep within. We have merely touched at the boundaries. Yet many of us often mistake acquaintance for love. To reach to someone's interior, we must first be able to reach our own. That alone is a challenge.

If we really want to meet another at his interior, we have to allow him to meet us at ours as well. This is a very scary thing, because we have to become completely open, vulnerable, and exposed. It is very risky to completely expose ourselves to others because we don't know how they will treat us; so fear steps in. And with fear, unconditional love is impossible.

In order to protect ourselves, we've built walls around us. These boundaries keep others from getting in; but they also prevent us from getting out.

When unconditional love is experienced, our individual walls disappear. We become so consumed with the very essence of each other that our physical forms become almost invisible. We venture deep within to each other's center. The relationship then becomes more meaningful, more spiritual, more deep. There are no struggles. All boundaries are removed. We simply blend together.

But, this type of relationship may seem almost impossible, because people don't trust each other. How can we trust others, unless we first learn to trust ourselves? It's understandable that we are afraid and apprehensive of completely opening to others, because people become bored quite easily. For instance, you expose yourself to another, who may enjoy you for a while; then your exterior become *familiar,* you are no longer *new.* Then the other becomes unappreciative, starts taking you for granted, starts seeking *newness.* This is where the difficulty begins. And the relationship is no longer interesting, no longer *new.*

It is a natural part of the human experience to learn and grow. Each of us grows at a different pace. Therefore, in some relationships, one can out grow the other. This doesn't make either individual good or bad, superior or inferior, better or worse. But the relationship can become destructive, if the situation is handle incorrectly, if one or the other is unable to be honest, to communicate openly, or to let go. Disrespect, abuse, or infidelity then becomes part of the relationship.

Each begins to blame the other for the chaos. In deep love, there is no room for this. Therefore, this relationship was never really love. Your interiors have never met-- just your exteriors. It was only an acquaintance, maybe a very intense and long-lasting one, but non the less, only an acquaintance.

To experience eternal *newness,* some adjustment has to take place. Both personalities have to grow together, or the relationship will experience constant turbulence. Many individuals are sadly mismatched in their relationships. This is not only unfortunate, but also a sad deprivation of unconditional and compatible love.

THE IMPORTANCE OF COMPATIBILITY

Love is kindness.
Kindness is respect and appreciation shown towards each

other. Compatible love does not come overnight. It has to be built. It involves consideration for each other's feelings. Compatibility entails passing love's difficult test-- overcoming selfishness, false pride, and unforgivingness. It is not always easy, but should always be kind-- not always exciting, but should always be warm. Sometimes it requires putting aside your own desires to accommodate your companion's. It is a trade off, a compromise. There must be a healthy balance between the minds, bodies, and spirits of both people involved.

Deep love walks hand-in-hand with contentment. A couple who truly loves radiates a magical force field. They glow with joy. Their union is blessed with an intense combination of understanding, tenderness, and passion. Well-mated lovers are truly lucky people. But luck is not what makes their bonding work. Mutual patience, trust, and compassion bind these two together.

They are compatible because they think alike. Only people who think on the same level can appreciate each other. They strive for similar causes, and support each other's ideas, ideals, and goals.

Many people falsely believe that opposites attract. Opposites may create initial curiosity, but eventually they repel each other. People should not be misled by initial curiosity, but should select companions who think along the same lines as themselves.

Without similar ground, the relationship is bound to fail. It may even last for years, but it will eventually fail. We would save ourselves from a lot of harmful situations if we would first get to know people well, and come to some form of compatible agreement, before embracing them into our hearts. Let me share a brief parable that was passed along to me by a wise mentor:

A little boy was on his way home from school and saw a pet curled up along the roadside. He didn't know what it was, but he was delighted to have it. He took it up and tucked it into his shirt pocket. He quickly ran home, anxious to share the news of his new pet. He joyously declared, "Mommy, come look what I found!" By the time the mother reached him, she found a dead child lying on the floor. Next to him was an uncoiled snake. Apparently, the serpent had been cold, it coiled itself, and was disguised. The unsuspecting child kindly embraced it into his bosom to give it warmth. After the cunning serpent used the innocent child to thaw, it coldly struck him dead!

Unbalanced relationships are just as harmful to us. They kill our innocence, our self-esteem, and our hopes; they kill our peace of mind.

If you are ever in a situation where your mate does not appreciate your worth, get out immediately. Your confidence will be damaged by continuous belittling or neglect. If he abuses you in any form, *run!* Do not hesitate for a moment.

Leave before it's too late. For, people do not change. They may alter their behavior to meet certain conditions, if it suits them, but eventually their true natures will resurface. For anyone to effectively change, they have to be reeducated and reprogrammed to move from one stage to another; otherwise, the seemingly new behavior is only a temporary measure. If you find you have to take at least ten steps backward, while he is unable to take even three forward, the disparity is too wide. This unbalance can never be harmonious for either of you. In all fairness to both of you, you should each find your own level of compatibility.

Compatible love does not hurt. In compatible unions, two individuals come together because they *want* to be with each other, not because they *need* to be.

Very often people hang on to incompatible relationships for fear of losing love. But they do not realize that in true love, there is no fear. There is no jealousy, no possessiveness, and no demanding; love is freely given.

You can never lose love. It is a part of your natural self, just like your heart is. Love is always with you. A certain person's love may be lost, but not love itself. Love for a particular person, can always be transformed into love for another.

What we should ask ourselves is, is it the *person* we really love, or is it the *love* which that person makes us feel

124

about ourselves that we actually desire?

Most of us will be surprised to discover that it is really the feeling of being in love which we crave, and not necessarily the particular person-- that he was only the vehicle by which we chose to transmute our own love to ourselves.

We enjoy the sharing of love because it gives us a sense of importance. The end of relationships is not pleasant. But after we have passed through the unpleasantness of letting go, and have become involved with another love, we barely remember the first one. We often times wonder what we ever saw in the person in the fist place, finally realizing that we were never compatible from the very beginning.

Time heals all wounds; and compatible love transcends all barriers.

HOW TO COPE WITH THE "HEARTBREAK"
OF A FAILED RELATIONSHIP

(This is for the sisters who are presently trying to cope with the pain felt from an estranged lover.)

You've tried your best in the relationship. You knew he wasn't the best for you, but you hung in there, hoping he would treat you better, or return the feelings you felt for him; but all of a sudden, things changed. He changed the course of things. He decided to move on. How do you cope? How do you keep on? How do you move on?

Day in, day out-- night after night, he monopolizes your thoughts. You can't get him out of your mind. Life feels meaningless. People tell you to have patience, and the right love will come along someday. But you don't want to hear that right now. You start to think of all the things "you could have done to keep him- to make him stay- to make it work." You think of all the good times you shared. How good he made you feel. How much you miss him. How very badly you need him right now. You daydream about him coming back into your arms, and how good it will feel. You wonder who he is with, what he is doing, and if he is thinking about you as much as you are thinking about him. You yearn for this man; your entire system is obsessed with his being.

As time passes, you begin to get tired of your own tears. You start to get upset with yourself for thinking of this man because you realize it's not bringing him back, and you're only making yourself feel ill. You start to fight the visions, thoughts, and memories of this estranged lover, and the enchanting times you spent together...... *Don't!* That's right- don't. Allow yourself to remember all the good times you shared. Enjoy your memories. But, be fair to yourself and give yourself equal time to visualize the bad, hurtful, and unhappy memories as well. Think of all the unfair and painful things he has done to you-- the things that made you mistrust him. The things that didn't make you feel good about yourself-- that made you feel uncomfortable, unwanted, and insecure. Visualize all the unpleasantness and embarrassment that this man has put you through. Think about the personality conflicts between the both of you. Then weigh it all up. Write your feelings down. Make a *good list,* and a *bad list* of your relationship with this individual. Was this relationship fair to you?

It may take some time to get to this point but, you should strive to hold no hard feelings against this person. Realize that he was unable to appreciate your worth. Don't be angry at him; instead feel compassion for him. Force yourself to really wish him the best. Turn the matter over to God. Know that you did your best, but you have to move on. Know within your very center that you deserve much better treatment than this.

Don't think of replacing him with someone else right away. Instead, concentrate on getting to know yourself better. How does this make you feel about yourself? How can you nurture *you?* What are you afraid of; is it loneliness? Talk it over with your intuitive, inner self. There's a *comforter* that we each have within us. It is a gift from God, as promised to us by our elder brother, the Divine Nazerene, "*And I pray the Father, and he shall give you another Comforter, that he may abide with you forever...I will not leave you confortless: I will come to you...Let not your heart be troubled, neither let it be afraid...if it were not so, I would have told you so."*

Our individual *comforter* is there to console us in all situations.   Whether we choose to term him or her a guardian angel, the Spirit of truth, our higher self, the Holy Ghost, our inner self, or intuitive self, it doesn't matter; the point is, she is there to guide and comfort us at all times.

Be open with your *comforter.* Let her know that you are afraid of being lonely, unloved, and of growing old alone. Talk to her as you would to a best friend. Ask for warmth, tranquillity, and guidance; then sleep on it.   Each time disturbing thoughts of this individual, or of any other situation that makes you afraid, surface, retreat to your inner *comforter.* Let her guide you.   Just take it one day at a time.   Eventually, you'll genuinely feel grateful to the estranged individual for releasing you to achieve more in life.

This was never compatible love. For compatible love is charitable.   As confirmed in Corinthians 13:4,5, *"Charity suffereth long, and is kind; charity envieth not; charity vaunteth not itself, is not puffed up. Doth not behave itself unseemly, seeketh not her own, is not easily provoked, thinketh no evil."* To sum it all up, compatible love does not hurt.

128

HOW COMPATIBLE ARE YOU WITH YOUR MATE?

The following twelve points can help you evaluate the depth of your present relationship. You can also use this format to review any past, or research any future ones. Use the meditation and visualization methods described in the "KNOW THYSELF" chapter. This will furnish you with a clear picture in order to honestly answer the following:

1. The things I like best about my mate are...
2. The things I dislike most about him are...
3. He stimulates my interest with ideas and thoughts in the following ways...
4. He does not stimulate my interest in the following ways...
5. He respects, admires, and appreciate my thoughts and feelings in these areas...
6. He fails to respect my thoughts and feelings in these areas...
7. I feel completely at ease, and can freely express myself to him about these issues...
8. I am uncomfortable, and unable to freely communicate with him about these issues...
9. He supports my goals, and urges me to pursue my interest in these ways...
10. He discourages my pursuit of the following goals...
11. I enjoy the way he makes me feel when...
12. I do not enjoy it when he...

After you've completed the twelve points, take some time to really think about each of your responses. Write an overview of your relationship. Then reverse the roles, and analyze yourself on your mate's behalf, using the same guidelines. Is the relationship productive and healthy for both of you? Are you happy, not so happy, or unhappy most of the time? If there are any uncomfortable differences, are you both willing to improve them together? To sum the whole evaluation up, ask yourself three very important questions:

1. Does his presence enrich my life in any way?
2. Is he looking out for my best interests?
3. Does he like me for the individual I am?

If you have answered "yes" to all three, then there is an excellent chance that he is the ideal mate for you. If you have answered "no" to any of the above, then ask yourself if it's fair to you, to be involved with someone who does not appreciate your inner worth?

You must be truthful with yourself when analyzing your relationship. Because people who travel on unequal roads can never appreciate each other. If we turn on the tap and expect to get hot water, and hot water flows, then it's all right. But if cold water comes, then something is wrong. We need to look into it. But most people don't. We rationalize that it's O.K., and the water will eventually become warm, but it

130

never does. And then when our relationships go wrong, we are horrified, when all along, we intuitively knew it was wrong, but we were afraid of letting go. Letting go is very difficult. It is probably one of the hardest things to do in life. But what's even harder on us is the hurt experienced from mis-matched relationships.

Always place a first class value on yourself. Accepting an incompatible relationship is like blending caviar with a platter of sardines. You are too valuable an individual to settle for a sardine-minded mate. A compatible union is one with another who is willing to blend his mind, body, and spirit with yours-- that you may both enjoy the beautiful totality of unconditional love on Earth.

THAT MAGIC TOUCH OF CREATIVE SEX

There is no way one can expect to maintain or create a wholesome relationship without addressing the topic of sex. While love is one of the most powerful form of the female energy, sex is one of the strongest form of the male energy. Generally speaking, while women may share sex in hopes of receiving love, men may share love in hopes of receiving sex. The sexual energy is a natural part of our equilibrium; It is the basic layer of our being. As it rises to higher levels, it journeys towards the interior, towards love. It becomes more compassionate, more sustaining, and more spiritual.

People have always been obsessed with sex, but never more so than they are today. The word "orgy" is Roman. There have been ancient cultures whose religions encouraged sex-- some Roman and Greek sects. Western religions-- from the 18th century on-- had repressed sex. But in today's civilization, after many years of suppression, people have become rebellious. Instead of *sexual repression, sexual obsession* has become the norm. Both are extremes; both are harmful.

Sex is a wonderful, important, and natural part of human relations, but if abused, it becomes greedy, dirty, and corrupt. People have sex for three reasons:

1. *Procreation* - To continue the human race
2. *Accommodation* - To feel wanted by satisfying another
3. *Recreation* - To have orgasms

If you were to ask ten different people their reasons for having sex, you'd most likely get ten different answers. However, each answer would fit within the three categories above. Test it for yourself. Take a few minutes to think about it. The first two are basically self-explanatory. Let us look into the third-- recreational sex to have orgasms.

An orgasm is the natural rising of the vibrations of the human system to meet the need of the body impulses. This is induced by mental, physical, and/or visual stimulation.

When it reaches the highest level-- the peak- -the climax, your thinking stops. At this exact moment, you are completely absorbed in the experience. This is the point of ecstasy-- the ultimate-- pure bliss. Because you become so deeply emerged into the experience, you are unable to concentrate. Your mind is blank. You experience perfect harmony. At this therapeutic moment you become completely uninhibited, completely free, and completely fulfilled.

It is because of moments like these, that sex, the stimulant, is one of the strongest of male desires. So powerful is this desire that relationships are either strengthened or weakened by it. For example, there are many people who are not properly suited for each other, but because of *good sex,* they stay together. Then they are those who are compatible in many areas, but due to lack of *good sex,* they are torn apart.

Can you count the number of times you've heard stories of men who have been married to beautiful, loving, and devoted wives for many years, and one day decide to trade in all they have accomplished together, for another woman? Or of the many, many men who portray ideal husbands, mates, or family men, but secretly maintain mistresses, or have extramarital affairs, or one-night stands with selections ranging from exclusive call girls to common street prostitutes? Whether these men are princes, paupers, or politicians, the results are the same. Unless they have psychological problems, they are cheating for the physical sex. Not just for the act of sex, but for the *creativity* of sex. Creative, recreational sex keeps relationships fresh, interesting and *new*.

Communicate openly with your present or future partner about his likes and dislikes. Let him know your desires and discomforts as well. Find out what turns him on. You shouldn't do anything which really makes you uncomfortable, but be willing to experiment a little. I cannot emphasize enough, how very important it is for you to have this knowledge, because many men are hypocritical with their mates. They'll place their mates on pedestals, and expect them to act saintly, but then these very same men indulge in unconventional sex with other women. This double standard is very dishonest and unfair, but it is constantly applied. Most men are so obsessed with creative, recreational sex, that they voluntarily risk their reputations and lives for it.

Frankly speaking, although you must never compromise yourself to your own discomfort, learn to be a "lady" in the open, but behind closed doors, become *creative* with your mate.

During an episode of The Oprah Winfrey Show on "why men cheat," one fellow proudly shared, "If a man eats steak everyday, he'll get bored. He'll sometimes want to try chicken or fish." Although his terminology for women may have been distasteful, the overall statement is very true, because of the human desire for *newness*. However, there are many creative ways to prepare steak, with *new* and invigorating ideas. Feed him *new* dishes with an ongoing menu of original and exciting herbs, spices, and garnishes-- as he in turn should do for you. If tastefully prepared, you mate's hunger can become so satisfied with his steak, that his desire for sampling chicken or fish may very well become an appetite of the past.

MISTAKES THAT BLOCK TRUE LOVE

Can a man be satisfied with one woman? The answer is yes. It depends on his values. If he is mentally steady, he can; if he is a variable character, he cannot.

Generally, men tend to be loose. A fantasy can catch them off-guard in a split second; and when they are caught off-guard, they do not think before they act.

It also depends on what a man is looking for in a woman. If he keeps straying, basically he's dissatisfied with something. Most men who have a lot of women are confused, but they won't tell you so. Multiple partners can serve as an escape from dealing with their insecurities. However, there are some men who simply enjoy sampling many women-- because so many women make it easy for them. Women are the ones who actually dictate sexual situations with men. If a man makes an advance to a woman, and she refuses, he has to back off. This is by no means meant to condone the behavior of men, but if women wouldn't give sex so readily, men wouldn't be so loose. They would have no choice, but to regain respect for women.

To introduce mistakes that block true love, the following is an excerpt from my first book, *The Fortune of Being Yourself:*

If you are a female in this society, you've been conditioned from birth to become a "wife." You've been told to "act like a lady," in hopes that "Prince Charming" would come along to rescue you. He would sweep you off your feet, take care of you, and you would "live happily ever after."

It is, therefore, quite natural for a woman to want an ideal mate to love, appreciate, and cherish her. Many women are involved in happy relationships and marriages. But many more are not. Some are still waiting for their fairy-tale romance to materialize. Others have given up hope of ever finding their "prince," and have settled for the "court jester" instead. Many compromise their ethics and resort to having affairs with someone else's mate. Still, others have chosen celibacy as a means of escaping the hurt felt when "Prince Charming" turns out to be "Prince Harm-ing."

There are many reasons for an unsuccessful relationship. Eight mistakes that block true love are:
Mistake #1: Pretending to be someone you are not
Mistake #2: Needing to be loved vs. wanting to be loved
Mistake #3: Fear of rejection
Mistake #4: "I want to marry a millionaire"

Mistake #5: Confusing sex with love

Mistake #6: "I no longer enjoy the relationship, but I continue because he is so gorgeous"

Mistake #7: "I want to leave him, but I can't make it on my own"

Mistake #8: "Maybe he will change in time"

(The Fortune of Being Yourself, p.30)

Women are prone to these mistakes for two reasons. One, they've been falsely led to believe that there is a shortage of men in today's society. So, they've placed men on pedestals, cherishing them as prized treasures, no matter how badly they themselves are treated. Many women are fearful that if they become too assertive, independent, or bold they will grow old alone. Women are made to feel incomplete if they are not married with children by the age of thirty. It has become a circus, like dangling bones in front of hungry puppies. It is pathetic that many men today have little or no respect for women. For instance, a man will tell a woman to have patience and give him a "little more time" to make up his mind, either about marrying her, or about giving up seeing another woman. The 'little more time," slips into weeks, then months, and then years; and he still sings the same song, and she still listens to the same lyrics. If women would just realize that they are being used, in these situations, and let men know that they value themselves highly, they would be amazed how things would turn around for them.

Second, many women are motivated by greed. They become weakened by money. They'll quickly trade sex in hopes of having their bills paid. Many women use their bodies to entrap a man in exchange for money. As time goes on, she may come to believe she is falling in love with him. Then when the man does not return the emotional feelings she expects, she is devastated! Can a person play with fire and not be burned? The man in this situation will usually leave as soon as another, more interesting "sex object" comes along. The physical aspect, without the mental and spiritual blending of a relationship, is lust, not love. These women measure the worth of a man by the car he drives, the position he holds, or the clothes he wears. It is definitely important to desire an ambitious companion who has a driving force for wanting to do well in life; but to choose a man based solely on his material possessions, is to court disaster. "All that glitters isn't gold." His inner worth could be "tarnished bronze."

I've heard women use such terms as, "I'm going to milk him like a cow," or "shuffle him like a deck of cards." I've heard men ask, "Why buy the cow when I can get the milk for free?" We all play these unnecessary games with each other-- men and women alike. We profess that we don't understand each other, but we are actually more alike than we are different. We all desire compatible love. If we would only take the effort to really get to know each other as friends, instead of viewing each other as challenges, we'd genuinely like each other more.

There is a simple solution to our coming together respectfully. It's so endearing, it has been termed golden. It states, "do unto others as you wish to be done unto you."

If we all would just make a little effort to apply this beautiful rule, our relations would be so much more meaningful and fulfilling.

THE KEY TO A GOOD RELATIONSHIP

Compatibility, yet individuality, is the key to a fulfilling relationship. It is to give of yourself, but not give up yourself. You both give your hearts, but not lose your hearts. Admire each other, but do not become each other. Enjoy your bonding, but do not crowd each other's space. You are two separate people who join together to enjoy common interests, but you still must allow each other room to express your own selves. You are able to enjoy your unrelated activities, but return to each other to share them. There is always room in your togetherness.

When you love, love kindly. Love genuinely. Love deeply. For, as Gibran shared so passionately in *The Prophet,* *"...let these be your desires...To know the pain of too much tenderness.. To wake at dawn with a winged heart and give thanks for another day of loving...And then to sleep with a prayer for the beloved in your heart and a song of praise upon your lips."*

7
A New Attitude

Ye are the salt of the earth: but if the salt have lost his savour…it is thenceforth good for nothing, but to be cast out, and to be trodden under foot of men…
Let your light shine so bright before men, that they may see your good works, and glorify your Creator which is in heaven.

St. Matthew 5:13:16

7

A New Attitude

Open your eyes, and look within you, my sisters. Realize that you are a very important part of this world. You have a vital role to fulfill on this planet-- not because you are Black, not because you are a woman, but simply because you *are*.

All humans are born on Earth for a purpose. Not just to be "good," as most institutions admonish, but to be good *for* something. For some greater purpose than the food we eat, the clothes we wear, or the possessions we accumulate. Most of us spend our entire lives striving to achieve material wealth in this physical world, but virtually ignore the richest treasures of all- our body temples- and the purposes that we were placed on Earth to achieve.

Do you believe we were given the miraculous gift of life, only to gain material things, and nothing else? No, sis, it's much deeper than that. Our lives are beautiful gifts from our Creator, to be used as opportunities to express ourselves on Earth. Not to express mundane principles as most of us do, but to express that which comes from the very depth of our centers. We must each find out from within, what we can uniquely contribute to the world. This should be our main aim in life.

Our individual contribution need not be to the entire human race, or even to an entire race of people; it can simply be to our individual household, our families, our circle of acquaintances, or our communities.

There is something within each of us that is unique. This is not an issue of physical appearances, or material possessions; it is much more meaningful than these surface values. How many of us are searching for real happiness inside? If we are not properly centered in the Creator's greater purpose for us, we can never truly achieve lasting happiness on this planet. We must strive to be happy in the now of today, for who can tell what life after this planet is like? Who has gone beyond and returned to share the experiences? Modern medicine tells of some individuals who claim they have experienced death for a few moments, and have then returned to life; all they are able to relate is that they saw a white light, and peaceful shadows. But what is a white light and shadows when we have the miracle of life and real people to relate with today? We must live our lives harmoniously and peacefully now, with our fellow human beings on the planet, while we still have life to do so. We must not take this for granted. More and more people are opening up to the concept of reincarnation. Some are even seeking "professed experts" to help them to contact their past lives. My question is, why should we seek to contact past lives, when we are having such difficulties dealing with our present ones? Instead, shouldn't living beings concentrate on making the best of their lives today?

Many people look into past life experiences, in hopes of being told that they were some queen, goddess, or advocate of great accomplishment, in order to flatter or soothe their egos. But even if we each were, so what? How can that help us in this life? There is a reason for the present-day amnesia we have about any past life experiences. Can you imagine if everyone started getting caught up in contacting past lives? There would be no reason for present lives. Do you realize the danger of these practices if used for selfish purposes? Some people believe that learning about their past life experiences can help them correct any mistakes-- clear up the "bad luck," karma, or difficulties they are presently facing. This is just another distraction from living right with our fellow humans today.

We must begin to see ourselves as part of a universal

145

plan. We each have the power within us, to mold our lives exactly the way we desire, in today's world. There is always help available for us to do this. That help comes from God, our Creator, which is within us. This is true no matter which religion we practice. As the beloved mystic Edgar Cayce expressed, *"...the church is within yourself and not in any pope or preacher, or in any building but in self! For thy body is indeed the temple of the living God, and the Christ becomes a personal companion in the mind and body; dependent upon the personality and the individuality of the entity as it makes practical application of the tenents and truths that are expressed."*

The Christ is an inner consciousness we each have the potential to cultivate. It is the love, peace, understanding, kindness, and charity that we show to our fellow human beings. Such love may seem like a dream, a myth, or some far-fetched hope, but this awareness actually dwells within each of us, as the Creator himself stated in Deuteronomy 31, *"For this commandment which I command thee this day, it is not hidden from thee, neither is it far off. It is not in heaven that thou shouldest say, Who shall go up for us to heaven, and bring it unto us, that we may hear, and do it? ...But the word is very nigh onto thee, in thy mouth, and in thy heart, that thou mayest do it."*

If we looked deeply within, we would eventually begin to see that ultimately, nothing really matters. Although it is very important for us to have a prosperous life on Earth--

with enough comfort, luxury, and money that we don't have to worry about how we will manage to pay our bills, or where our next meal will come from-- if money becomes an obsession, and we are guided by greed, jealously, envy, hatred, worry, fear, cruelty, gossip, or dishonesty, it is not conducive to our well-being.   We'll never have peace of mind.

Nothing in this world is worth the price of our peace of mind. Even if we each lived in a palace, we could never enjoy it if we didn't have peace of mind.   *"For what is a man profited, if he shall gain the whole world, and lose his own soul?"* Peace of mind is the seat of the soul. Instead of going through life accumulating possessions that we must eventually leave here, wouldn't it be better to focus on acquiring spiritual qualities that will remain with us throughout eternity?

We may not have any control over when we come into this world, and none over when we are to leave, but we have every bit of control over our individual lives while we are now on the planet. It is our responsibility to ourselves, and to our Creator, to fulfill the individual purposes we were each incarnated on Earth for.   That purpose is to love our Creator, love ourselves, and love our fellow human beings, regardless of race, nationality, or form. If we dislike anyone for any reason, it shouldn't be for any of the before mentioned qualities; it should be because of a specific behavior or mannerism that person has that may be harmful

147

to us. We must strive to relieve the suffering of individuals and to bring joy to friends and strangers alike.

A true test of love is how we treat our neighbors. People claim they love God. Yet they have never seen God. God said to love our fellow human beings. People don't love their fellow human beings, then how can they love God? Then the love they claim is hypocritical. This doesn't mean we should all be goody-goodies and not be able to tell someone to go to hell if they deliberately try to harm us. However, remember this, there is a lot of good in the worst of us, and a lot of bad in the best of us. So let us not disrespect each other based on our own limited exposure and selfish purposes. For it was given, *"If ye love me, keep my commandments; for they are not grievous to bear. For I will bear them with thee, I will wipe away thy tears; I will comfort the brokenhearted, I will bring all to those in the ways that are in the Wisdom of God..."*

To obtain peace of mind on Earth, we must have a three-way balance among God (love), health, and money. If we are frustrated, we must not take it out on another. One of the most common forms of frustration is lack of money. If we have only one dollar to spend, let's not spend it all today. Many of us spend all today and leave ourselves broke for tomorrow-- which leaves us in a state of want and aggression. We must not be envious of what other people have, or be sorrowful thinking of what we haven't got. When we become frustrated about our situations, we should think of the old, wise saying, "I felt sorry for myself because I didn't have any shoes, until I met the person who didn't have any feet."

Another source of frustration is other people's opposition. If our opinions are opposed, we resent the ones opposing them. We expect what we say to be accepted without question. But life doesn't work like that. Every person in life has an individual opinion. We must all be tactful and wise in order to function. We must view problems openly, and face them squarely, instead of painting pictures suitable to our own selfish desires.

We must learn to open up to new ideas and concepts to get along with people; but we all seem to be so closed off. We need to entertain open minds, regardless of how much we may know about a subject, because there is always more than one path to solve any problem. People shouldn't criticize anyone or anything unless doing so makes it better for that person. If it serves no useful purpose, leave it alone. Try this experiment out for yourself: Attempt to go just one full day without saying anything bad about anyone, and see how rewarding your day will be.

If people could manage to drop their individual masks and egos, they would be surprised at the freedom they'd experience. What are we really gaining by trying to out-do and belittle each other on Earth? Is it nicer clothing, homes, furnishing, more money, or some other material article? As

Christ so eloquently put it, *"Lay not up for yourselves treasures upon earth, where moth and rust doth corrupt, and where thieves break through and steal: But lay up for yourselves treasures in heaven, where neither moth nor rust doth corrupt, and where thieves do not break through and steal: For where your treasure is, there will your heart be also."*

How little we must think of ourselves, if we place more value on the treasures of the Earth, instead of the treasures of our peace of mind.

To obtain peace of mind, is to experience heaven on Earth. It is very true that we must have money and certain material possessions in order to obtain peace of mind, because if we don't have ample money, we will not be able to concentrate on the joys of life. However, we must not become so consumed with the possession money, that it actually ends up possessing us.

Earthquakes, storms, fires, and other natural disasters are facts of life throughout the world. Many people have lost their entire possessions, in a split second. But they still have hope, because they still have their lives. For, there are just as many who were not fortunate enough to keep their lives, and were wiped away instantly, by these wraths of nature. People don't seem to realize the importance of life.

Sis, I hope you now realize the importance of your life,

and the lives of all humans on Earth. Let's give respect to others, that we may in turn gain respect from others. There is enough space and wealth on the planet for all of us humans to enjoy the happy, beautiful, and fulfilling lives which God created us to have.

Go thy way, eat thy bread with joy, and drink thy wine with a merry heart...Let thy garments always be white; and let thy head lack no ointment. Live joyfully with whom thou lovest...for this is thy portion in this life, and in thy labour which thou takest under the sun... Let us hear the conclusion of the whole matter; Love God, and keep his commandments: for this is the whole duty of man. For God shall bring every work into judgment, with every secret thing, whether it be good, or whether it be evil.

Ecclesiastes

hyacinths for the mind

We can eliminate all fears, and reprogram our minds to achieve our individual desires.

We wrongly *underestimate* the value of our own thinking, while we falsely *overestimate* the thinking of others.

Our minds absorbs and react to whatever we put into them.

Greater is that which is in us, than that which is in the world.

You must live your life with expectation; expect your mind to perform any task you ask it to.

There are many solutions to any one problem.

The human mind is a beautiful instrument. It can be programmed for victories or defeats.

Affirm exactly what you want and let it manifest through your unwavering power of concentration and belief.

We can rewrite, direct, and produce our own chose performances, at any time we desire.

Our minds are the only possessions we have total control over in life.

The opinions of others cannot be absorbed into our thinking if we make conscious efforts to refuse them.

True contentment can only come from within-- when we learn to become at peace with ourselves.

Is man therefore greater than his Creator, to elect himself authority on which of God's creations is ideal and which is not?

People's behavior can be ugly, but their forms are all beautiful, no matter how varied, they are all of equal value.

We are all passengers on this oversized boat called Earth. And whether we sink or survive depends on how well we can paddle together.

There is no intrinsic difference between people. It all depends on the upbringing, exposure, and basic guidance.

How ridiculous of anyone to discriminate against a certain sector of the population, simply because the Creator has colored their skins with various shades of beautiful brown.

Although we cannot prevent other ethnic groups from throwing discriminating remarks at us, we can, however, love, respect, and appreciate ourselves to the extent where things said would have no impact.

If Blacks do not care for each other, which other ethnic group can we honestly expect to do so?

It is knowledgeable to know where we have been, but more importantly, is where we are going.

Scarcity and want deprives the mind of functional thought. It breaks people down to levels of beasts.

How can the hungry child learn? How can the distraught personality function?

If a man is without shelter, or a woman cannot pay her bills, how can they listen and pass on information towards the healing of a race?

Today we need a total awareness, both from the educated and non-educated classes to reverse the downfall of the Black race.

The sooner we realize that the varying shades of our melanic skins does not matter, but the main issue is our behavior pattern, the sooner we can come together to find effective solutions.

It is very easy to point a finger at someone else, but this will not make us any better.

If we can *conceive* the thought in our minds, and can *believe* it in our hearts, then we can surely *achieve* it in our lives.

Upcoming title from KOLA PUBLISHING

The Right Spot
Insights to women, from men, on love, sex, relationship, friendship and marriage

For further information, contact:
KOLA PUBLISHING
610 Fifth Avenue
P.O. Box 4739
New York, NY 10185-0040